ELECTRICAL WORK

ELECTRICAL WORK

A Handbook of Tools, Materials,
Methods, and Directions

BY

JOHN F. NOWAK

Author — Practical Residential Wiring
Administrator — Veterans and Reconversion Training Program
Teacher — Electrical Installation and Practice,
Board of Education, New York City

D. VAN NOSTRAND COMPANY, INC.

TORONTO   NEW YORK   LONDON

NEW YORK

D. Van Nostrand Company, Inc., 250 Fourth Avenue, New York 3

TORONTO

D. Van Nostrand Company (Canada), Ltd., 228 Bloor Street, Toronto

LONDON

Macmillan & Company, Ltd., St. Martin's Street, London, W.C. 2

CONTENTS

INTRODUCTION

Electrical installations, devices, and appliances frequently require repairs and adjustments, which range in complexity from the simplest manipulation to the most extensive rewiring. Serious electrical trouble may, of course, require the services of a skilled worker, an electrician. However, the average home mechanic may do quite a few electrical jobs himself, gaining experience with practice until he attains a fair degree of proficiency.

Before undertaking any electrical work whatever, the home mechanic should be thoroughly familiar with the requirements of his local regulations regarding this work. Electrical installation is a licensed trade in many communities, and thus comes under supervision. A code of standard practice known as the National Electrical Code governs nationwide installations. In addition, many large communities have their own code which supersedes the National Code in that locality. An example of a local code would be the Electrical Code of the City of New York, Title B of Chapter 30 of the Administrative Code, which governs all electrical installations in the New York Metropolitan Area.

Since some local codes not only specify how the details of the work should be done, but require that all new installations should be made by a licensed electrician, it is most important that everyone undertaking electrical work be familiar with his local regulations. If it happens that the reader lives in a remote place in which there are virtually no local regulations governing electrical work, then he is urged to follow the National Electrical Code which may be purchased at a nominal cost from the National Board of Fire Underwriters at Chicago, Ill. This national code has been adhered to throughout this entire Electrical Work book.

It is to be noted that most code restrictions refer specifically to new installations. In most communities repair and maintenance can be done by anyone in the home. However, even the simplest repair requires an understanding of elementary electrical principles and, therefore, the first chapter in this book will be devoted to that subject. Needless to say, electrical theory will be treated in this book only briefly; for more complete presentations the reader is referred to the various textbooks on this subject, including such well known publications as "Swoope's Lessons in Practical Electricity" and Burn's "Electricity."

In the arrangement of this book, Chapter 1 gives, as stated above, a brief sketch of certain electrical principles which should be understood thoroughly before any electrical work is undertaken. Chapter 2 describes the tools most commonly used by the electrician in residential work — especially those tools which form part of the electrician's kit. Chapter 3 explains and illustrates various general operations in electrical work, which will be used frequently throughout all the later chapters in this Electrical book. These practical skills include splicing, soldering, taping, and other common operations.

Chapter 4 covers the various signaling systems used in the home, including bells, buzzers, door openers, and several similar devices. First, the apparatus used in each system is described, then the wiring circuit of each system is explained, and finally, one complete installation is described in full detail, covering every step of the work. Chapters 5 and 6 deal, respectively, with BX Cable and Conduit Wiring. In each case, the Code Regulations are briefly discussed. Then the materials used are described, and three complete projects are fully explained. These projects have been planned to introduce to the reader the greatest possible number of practical operations and "tools of the trade," so that he can refer to them in connection with any similar job he may undertake.

Chapter 7 deals with portable electrical appliances such as the vacuum cleaner, electric iron, and toaster, and fixed electrical equipment, such as the farm lighting plant, fans, pumps, and so on, as well as the various control devices that are necessary for their operation. The aim of this chapter is to give the reader a clear understanding of all these types of equipment, with the greatest possible number of practical suggestions and hints for adjustment and trouble shooting. Care has been taken to stop short of giving detailed discussions of individual models, and to avoid involving the reader in work that requires special tools or equipment.

Chapter 8 discusses suitable wiring methods for ungrounded interior wiring systems, such as Open Wiring on Insulators, Concealed Knob and Tube Wiring, and Non-metallic Sheathed Cable Wiring.

Chapter 1

BRIEF SKETCH OF ELECTRICAL PRINCIPLES

Generation of Electricity . . . Voltage and the Volt . . . Current and the Ampere . . . Ohm's Law . . . Resistance and the Ohm . . . Fuses and Circuit Breakers . . . Electrical Insulation . . . Heat Produced by the Electrical Current . . . Minimum Wire Sizes . . . Electrical Energy and Power . . . Alternating Currents . . . Parallel and Series Circuits . . . Counter Electromotive Force and the Starting Box

In order to do any work whatever on electrical circuits or equipment, it is desirable to understand some of the properties of electric currents. The discussion in this chapter will outline these electrical principles in sufficient detail to help the home owner or the home craftsman apply them to an understanding of the electrical repairs and installations which are described in the later chapters of this book. While the space available here is not sufficient for more than the merest outline of electrical principles, as they apply to small house wiring and connections, the reader is advised most strongly to read this chapter carefully before undertaking any of the electrical work.

The electric lines that radiate from the power station are spoken of as power lines, because they transmit the power produced by the generators in the central station. Any "live" wire, however remote, in the home or elsewhere, has behind it this constant source[1] of power, which may be used to furnish heat, light, or mechanical energy, and which must always be confined to proper pathways.

Generation of Electricity. In many respects, the action of an electrical generator may be compared to that of a water pump which is delivering water into a pipe line for distribution to various points along the line. The action of a water pump produces a difference in pressure between its outlet side and its inlet side. Similarly, an electrical generator may be pictured as causing a flow of electricity through a distribution system, and also as producing a difference in electrical pressure between its outlet side and its inlet side.

This electrical pressure, or rather pressure difference, at the generator,

[1] For bell circuits and other signal systems in the home, batteries may be used to furnish current.

causes the electricity to flow through the entire distributing and consuming
system that is served by the generator or group of generators.

Voltage and the Volt.   The unit used in measuring electrical pressure, or
pressure difference, is the volt.   This unit is most important in household
electrical work, partly because most electrical equipment used in the home,
is designed to operate at a fixed electrical pressure difference, or voltage.   Of

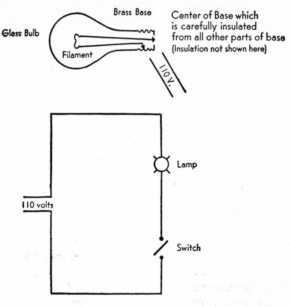

FIG. 6.1.   Simple lamp circuit.

course, the designed voltage varies with the equipment; the great generators
used in power plants may operate at, for example, 6600 volts, or 13,200 volts,
while electrical devices used in the home are commonly designed for an electrical pressure of 110 volts.   The designed voltage for all electrical equipment
is plainly marked upon it — this voltage figure is etched into the glass surface
of incandescent lamps, it is stated clearly upon the nameplates of motors, etc.
(While incandescent lamps and other equipment for use in the home are
designed to operate at 110 volts, they are commonly marked 120 volts,
because they can be operated safely at small overvoltages, which result from
voltage fluctuations in the line or in the house.)   The important consideration is to be absolutely sure that every piece of electrical apparatus is used in
a circuit carrying the designed voltage, because at materially lower voltages,

the equipment will operate inefficiently, or not at all, while higher voltages are destructive.

One reason why excess voltages are destructive will be apparent if we consider the operation of an ordinary incandescent lamp. The simple circuit of this lamp, shown in Fig. 6.1, consists of a single coil of filament wire, which is so connected to the metal part of the lamp that an insulated electrical circuit exists through the lamp. Now if an electrical pressure difference, or voltage, is applied to the two ends of this circuit, at their connections in the lamp socket, current will flow through the wire in the lamp. The greater the electrical pressure difference, or voltage, the greater will be the current of electricity. Since the filament inside the lamp has been designed to carry safely the current that will flow when 110 to 120 volts are applied, then the greater current that would result from a higher voltage might easily burn out the wire.

Current and the Ampere. Ohm's Law. Following this line of reasoning, an important relationship applying to electric currents can be reached. It was stated above that the greater the voltage that is applied to the same wire, the greater will be the current that flows through it. Now suppose the lamp described above were to be replaced by another lamp which contains a shorter filament wire of the same material and size. That is, suppose 110 volts is applied across the ends of a wire that is 4″ long, and then that the test is repeated by applying 110 volts across a piece of the same wire that is only 3″ long. The current will increase as the wire is shortened, because the resistance of the wire to passage of current decreases as its length decreases. This is reasonable, because a fixed electrical pressure difference could be expected to force more current through a short pathway than a long one — just as a larger stream of water would be obtained out of a short pipe than a long one, if the same water pressure were applied to both.

The relationship between electrical pressure difference, current, and resistance follows directly from the preceding paragraphs. In an electrical conductor, the strength of the current depends upon the pressure difference between the ends of the conductor, and also upon the resistance of the conductor. (Instead of the term "pressure difference" which we have used to present the conception, the term "potential difference" is used in electrical work, and it will be used hereafter.) The larger the potential difference, and the lower the resistance of the conductor, the greater will be the current.[1] Experience with direct currents has shown that the current in a closed,[1]

---

[1] That is, the pathway is entirely closed except in the technical sense that its ends are bridged by a potential difference, and not by an electromotive force.

metallic path is directly proportional to the potential difference, and inversely proportional to the resistance of the path. This relationship is called Ohm's Law, and is easiest to understand when expressed as an equation:

$$I = \frac{E}{R}, \quad \text{which may be written,} \quad R = \frac{E}{I}, \quad \text{or} \quad E = IR,$$

in which, I is the current, expressed in amperes,

E is the potential difference, expressed in volts,

R is the resistance, expressed in ohms.

This formula introduces the unit of current, the *ampere*, and the unit of resistance, the *ohm*. For the absolute meaning of these units, like that of the *volt*, the reader is referred to electrical textbooks. For present purposes, they may be used simply as convenient means of measurement.

Resistance and The Ohm. Let us apply Ohm's Law to a simple D.C. circuit, consisting of a small incandescent lamp, which is operating in a test circuit, so that the applied voltage and the current can be measured. The current is 0.36 ampere when the voltage is 110 volts. What is the resistance?

Since R is to be found, choose from the three expressions of Ohm's Law the relationship which gives R, that is, the relationship, $R = \frac{E}{I}$, and substitute the known values. Thus, in the above problem, $R = \frac{110}{0.36}$ ohms. Dividing 110 by 0.36, R is 306 ohms.

Now, take another type of problem. Suppose the lamp has a lower resistance, what will be the current if the voltage remains at 110 volts? Suppose, for example, that the resistance of this new lamp is one half the value found in the preceding problem, or 153 ohms. Then what will the current be?

To solve this problem, refer again to the three forms of the statement of Ohm's Law and choose the relationship which gives the current. It is $I = \frac{E}{R}$. Thus, in this problem, $I = \frac{110}{153}$. Dividing 110 by 153, find that I is 0.72 ampere.

Now, by referring to the two problems solved above, it will be seen that by halving the resistance in a simple D.C. circuit, we have doubled the current.

This is what is meant in the statement of Ohm's Law by the words "the current is inversely proportional to the resistance." From this relationship, it is easy to see why a short circuit is so dangerous. For if a low resistance path should be established between two conductors differing in electrical potential, or voltage, a relatively great current will flow. The lower the resistance of the path, the greater will be the current. The resistance of a tool blade, for example, is only a very small fraction of an ohm per inch. If, due to carelessness or accident, besides the inexcusable error of working on a live circuit, the tool blade should be in contact with two wires differing in potential by 110 volts, a momentary current of thousands of amperes would flow. It would last only momentarily, because it would soon destroy part of the circuit. Water is another possible cause of short circuits, because as it leaks into walls or floors, it dissolves materials which make it an excellent conductor.

Fuses and Circuit Breakers. To protect against damage by short circuits, special devices called circuit breakers or fuses are installed. Their use is compulsory in all codes governing electrical installation. They act to break the circuit when the current exceeds a specified amperage. Circuit breakers, which are used only on large installations, operate by induction, and fuses, which are used in the home, act by simple melting of a high-resistance material which has a low melting point. Fuses will be discussed in detail later in this book.

Electrical Insulation. It has been apparent during much of the foregoing discussion, that electrical resistance plays a most important part in the use of electricity. The resistance of the conductors and apparatus determines the current that will flow in the circuit, assuming that a given potential difference is applied to the circuit. Most home circuits have one wire at a potential of 110 volts, and the other wire at 0 volts, or ground.[1] Where this system is used (on A.C.), the Codes require that the 0-volt wire be connected to the ground at frequent and clearly specified points. The first wire, which carries the electrical potential of 110 volts, must be carefully protected from direct contact with metallic parts of plumbing, heating and other systems including the building structure to prevent accidental "grounds." The wire is given mechanical protection by the metal conduit in which it is encased. It is given electrical protection by its insulation,

---

[1] Of course, there are other systems used in some places, such as the 220-volt, three-wire system, which uses 110-volt equipment, and so might be confused with a simple 110-volt supply. Since this would have disastrous results, the voltage supplied should be checked with the electric power company, if there is any doubt whatever of its value.

which is a material or combination of materials having so great a resistance that, for all practical purposes, they are nonconductors of electricity. Rubber and related materials, textile fibers, porcelain, and glass are among the materials which have good insulating qualities. Electrical insulation is discussed in detail later in this book.

Heat Produced by the Electric Current. Just as it is important to insulate wires well to prevent any stray currents from leaking through the house and causing danger of fire or other damage, so it is equally important to keep the resistance of the conducting wires low. The purpose of the conductor wires is to carry the current and apply the voltage to the various incandescent lamps, motors, and other electrical equipment. In other words, the purpose of the wires is to deliver the power to the point of use, with as little "line loss" as possible. Line loss is objectionable not only because it represents an expense to the consumer, but also because it produces heat, in the same way that a loss of mechanical power by friction would be dissipated as heat. The heat produced by electrical line loss is especially objectionable, because it is formed inside the conduits that run right through the walls of the house. Therefore, since this line loss is determined partly by the resistance of the wire, it is most necessary to understand the factors which determine wire resistance, before undertaking electrical work in the home.

Minimum Wire Sizes. The resistance of an electrical conductor is substantially determined by three major factors: (1) the material of which the conductor is made, (2) the length of the conductor, and (3) its size (cross-sectional area). As far as the home owner is concerned, the first two of these factors are fixed and offer no choice. All ordinary wire is made of copper, and the length of wire used depends upon the wiring diagram, which has been made as direct as permitted by the location of switches, lamps, and other outlets, and by the code requirements. Therefore, the only available means of reducing the resistance of the electrical conductors, which distribute current in the home, is to increase their size (cross-sectional area). As the resistance of these electrical conductors is reduced by increasing their size, the heat produced in the conductors when they are carrying the required current is also reduced. On the other hand, the use of wire, in house circuits, that is too small in size will cause dangerous heating in the conduits which run through the walls of the house. For this reason, the codes specify carefully the minimum sizes of conductors which may be used in the various circuits found in the home. In all the installations to be described in this section, the requirements of the National Electrical Code will be followed.

Electrical Energy and Power. The measurement of electrical energy is important to the home owner chiefly because he pays for electricity upon the basis of the quantity of electrical energy consumed. In a simple D.C. circuit, the energy consumed is found by multiplying the voltage applied across the circuit by the current entering the circuit, and by the time. The equation is as follows:

D.C. Energy   =   Potential Difference $\times$ Current $\times$ Time
(In watt hours)   (In volts)   (In amperes)   (In hours)

For example, an incandescent lamp operating at 110 volts and taking a current of 0.36 ampere will consume 40 watt hours for every hour it burns. To convert watt hours to kilowatt hours, divide by 1000.

Alternating Currents. It should be noted that the above equation was stated to apply to a simple D.C. circuit. To compute the energy used in a single-phase A.C. circuit, it is necessary to add another quantity to the above equation, as follows:

A.C. Energy = Potential Difference $\times$ Current $\times$ Time $\times$ Power Factor
(In watt hours)   (In volts)   (In amperes)   (In hours)

The power factor is a number which is determined by the nature of the circuit. If the circuit contained only resistance, and no inductance or capacitance, the value of the power factor would be 1. While no circuit is ever totally without inductance or capacitance, their numerical values are relatively low as compared with the value of the resistance in the average home circuit. Therefore, it is possible to compute, fairly closely, the energy used in the average home A.C. circuit by ignoring the effect of inductance and capacitance entirely, and by taking the power factor at a value of 1. In that case, the equation for A.C. energy that is given above becomes the same as the equation for D.C. energy because, if the power factor is 1, it does not change the value obtained by multiplying the other quantities, and may be omitted.

There are many other properties of A.C. circuits, besides the energy consumption, which may be considered from the same standpoint as D.C. circuits, by ignoring the effect of inductance and capacitance. It is fortunate for our present purposes that this is so, because the principles governing A.C. circuits are far beyond the scope of any brief treatment. Therefore, this brief outline of electrical principles has been prepared from the standpoint of D.C. theory, because the conceptions and the practical working

principles developed in this discussion are perfectly valid for the ordinary
A.C. circuit found in the home. This is, however, decidedly not true in
factories or other large installations, or in cases where the use of special
equipment adds a substantial amount of inductance or capacitance to the
circuit.

Parallel and Series Circuits. The electrical circuits which have been
discussed so far in this chapter have contained only a single incandescent
lamp or other type of electrical equipment. In a home circuit, however,

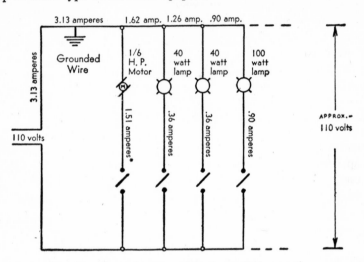

Fig. 6.2. House circuit containing four units in operation.

In calculating current taken by vacuum cleaner, we have taken motor efficiency at 75%.

there will usually be found a number of lamps and other types of equipment.
In order to supply them with electricity, at their rated voltage and amperage,
it is necessary to use a type of circuit which makes provision for these requirements. The type of circuit that is used in home wiring under all but the
most exceptional circumstances, is the parallel or multiple system.

In Fig. 6.2, there is shown a portion of a house circuit containing four units
in operation. These units, that are drawing current at the time, consist of
one 100-watt incandescent lamp, two 40-watt incandescent lamps, and one
vacuum cleaner motor of ⅙ horsepower. By reference to the figure, it will be
seen that each of the four units is connected across the full line voltage.
This is the distinguishing characteristic of the parallel method of connection.
The two wires, which have a potential difference of 110 volts, run to each

of the units, and each unit is connected in a branch circuit of its own with its own switch. The current in each branch circuit is determined by the requirements of the unit of equipment in that branch circuit. Figure 2 also shows the current taken by the unit in each circuit. It will be seen that there is always one part of the main circuit which must carry the total current used in the branches. This fact emphasizes the importance of using conductors of adequate size in house wiring, as required by the various codes, and as specified in the projects and directions given in the later chapters of this book.

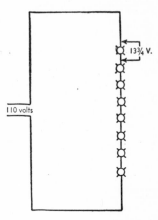

FIG. 6.3. Connecting electrical apparatus in series.

Another method of connecting electrical apparatus is the series system. It is very infrequently used in house wiring, but is occasionally found of value for special purposes, such as connecting Christmas-tree lights. By reference to Fig. 6.3, it will be seen that in this method of connection, the full line voltage is not applied to each unit of equipment, as was the case in the parallel method of connection. In this series circuit, a number of units in series are connected across the line. From this diagram, it is evident that the same small current flows through each of the eight lamps, and that the voltage applied to each lamp is only about one eighth of the line voltage, or about 13 or 14 volts.

Counter Electromotive Force and the Starting Box. This chapter will conclude by returning to the subject of electrical potential. Electrical potential may be produced in a number of ways. Mere rubbing of a cat's fur is sufficient to produce a potential of static electricity. Chemical action may be used to produce and maintain an electrical potential, as in the dry cell and the storage battery. By far the greater part of the world's electricity is obtained by the production and maintenance of an electrical potential in the dynamo or electrical generator.

The dynamo converts mechanical power into electrical power. In the operation of the dynamo, a steam turbine, water wheel, or internal combustion engine applies power to the generator, causing its armature to rotate, so that the electric wires on the armature continually move through a magnetic or electro-magnetic field. This produces an electrical potential (better called an electromotive force) in the dynamo, which causes current to flow throughout the circuit. In other words, a generator produces an electromotive force and an electric current from mechanical power. A motor operates in the reverse manner to produce mechanical power from an applied voltage and current. The motor, however, also produces, as it rotates and does work, an electromotive force (e.m.f.) of its own which opposes the electromotive force of the generator, or the applied voltage of the line. Therefore, the resistance of the armature winding of an electric motor must be low, because the voltage of the line is partly counteracted by this counter e.m.f. which the motor develops when rotating. But when the motor is not rotating, it produces no counter e.m.f., and so its low resistance armature winding will take an excessive current in starting.

This problem is solved by means of the rheostat, or starting box, which is connected to many motors. The function of the starting box is to add resistance to a circuit of an electric motor when the motor is starting, and to permit this resistance to be decreased in steps as the motor comes up to speed. In starting a motor that is so connected, it is necessary to make sure that the handle of the starting box is in the OFF position before throwing the switch. The handle of the starting box is then moved slowly from this first position (highest resistance) to the last position where the current flows directly to the motor without meeting any resistance at all in the starting box. This method of starting motors brings them up to speed safely, without damage from excessive current.

Chapter 2

~~~~~~

ELECTRICIAN'S TOOLS

The Pocketknife . . . Screwdrivers . . . Pliers . . . Saws . . . Hammers . . . Bit Brace and Wood Bits . . . Chisels . . . Star Drill . . . Center Punch . . . Plumb Bob . . . Files . . . Rules . . . Plaster Knife . . . Floor Steel . . . Snake . . . Alcohol Torch . . . Hand Drill, Twist Drill, Reamers, and Taps . . . Bending Hickey . . . Spirit Level . . . Awl or Ice Pick . . . Scriber . . . Pipe Wrenches . . . Stock and Die . . . Vise . . . Standard Electrical Symbols

The tools required in electrical work depend, of course, upon the type of work in which the particular electrician is engaged. Installation and repair of industrial machinery will require various tools rarely used elsewhere; while electricians who spend a large part of their time servicing a particular type of equipment, such as electrical refrigerators, will have certain tools which are specialized for that equipment.

There are a number of tools, however, that are commonly found in the kit of the electrician whose work is concerned largely with small house installation. These tools will be discussed in this chapter, as well as a few shop tools that are used very often in electrical work. Many of them are familiar to persons who have had only limited experience but, nevertheless the discussions here will be of value, because they will deal with the types and sizes of these tools needed in electrical work, and with the actual purpose and manner of their use by the practical electrician.

The **pocket knife** is one of the most frequently used tools in practical electrical work. It is well worth while to purchase a good pocket knife, which has two or three blades that are made of high quality steel. One of the blades should be quite broad, and the other blade or blades should be narrower and not too sharp. A pocket knife should never be carried in any pocket with a blade open. When not in use the knife should be kept closed. A fair cutting edge may be obtained on a knife blade by stroking the blade several times against the metal shank of a screwdriver or the surface of a common brick.

The common **screwdriver** is a tool used frequently by the electrician.

13

In fact, it is desirable to have three sizes of screwdrivers, with blade lengths of approximately 3″, 6″, and 8″, and with corresponding blade widths of about ¼″, 5⁄16″, and ⅜″. At least one of these screwdrivers should be the type that has an insulated handle.

A metal handle screwdriver, one which includes the handle and blade all in one, will be found very useful since it can be struck by a hammer without serious damage. Such a screwdriver is handy for tapping and prying. The importance of having several screwdrivers is evident from the fact that the electrician finds it necessary, not only to install new screws, but to renew old ones, which are frequently "rusted in" and difficult to start.

Pliers. So great are the number of uses which the electrician finds for pliers, that his kit should contain at least four pairs of pliers, representing three different types. It is recommended that there be two pairs of side-cutting pliers. The 6″ size and the 8″ size of side-cutting pliers will be sufficient for most purposes. It is most helpful to have a pair of diagonal-cutting pliers, in which the cutting edges are oblique instead of straight; the 6″ size will probably be found the most helpful. The kit should also contain a pair of gas pliers.

Saws. Both the hack saw and the keyhole saw are essential tools in the electrician's kit. The hack saw should be of the adjustable variety, that is, the type in which the frame can be shortened, whenever necessary, to work in narrow corners and other tight places. The hack saw should be provided with a wide variety of blades having various tooth sizes and tooth spacings.

The keyhole saw is preferably one of about 10″ in length of blade, with the teeth filed similarly to those of a crosscut saw.

Hammers. The electrician's kit should contain both a carpenter's hammer and a machinist's hammer. The carpenter's hammer is of the familiar claw type. The 12″ size will be found most helpful in electrical work. The machinist's hammer is the ball-peen hammer. The 16 oz. size which is recommended there is the best and will be found the most helpful for the electrician.

Bit Brace and Wood Bits. For the great number of wood drilling operations which are necessary in electrical installation, a good bit brace or hand brace, with a wide variety of bits, is essential equipment. A bit brace of medium size and ratchet type is preferable. For electrical work the brace should be chosen with a wide sweep of at least 12″. A number of wood bits should be available for use with this brace. The type of bit known as "electrician's bit," is preferable. However, this bit is usually obtained only in three sizes, $\frac{5}{8}''$, $\frac{11}{16}''$, and $\frac{3}{4}''$. Since it is also desirable to have two smaller bits, wood bits may be used instead of the electrician's bit on all but the heaviest work, such as drilling sills and heavy beams. It is also desirable to have one or more expansion bits. These bits are used for drilling large holes, such as those required to install rigid conduit.

An accessory to the bit brace which should be in every electrician's kit is the bit extension, which is illustrated in Fig. 6.4. The bit extension is inserted in the bit brace, between brace and bit, in order to lengthen the "reach" of this tool. The bit extension is essential for drilling in inaccessible places, such as

FIG. 6.4. Bit extension.

under floors, above ceilings, etc. The extension shown in the illustration has sufficient strength to drive a bit up to 1″ in diameter, but is small enough to follow a $\frac{5}{8}''$ bit. The accurately shaped recess in the chuck accommodates the shank of the bit, which is held by drawing the holding sleeve against the corners of the square.

Chisels. Both wood chisels and metal chisels are essential tools in the electrician's kit. Wood chisels are used so frequently that at least three of them should be obtained. The $\frac{1}{4}''$ size, the $\frac{1}{2}''$ size, and the 1″ size constitute a good selection for all ordinary purposes. A style of chisel preferred by electricians, especially in the larger sizes, is the heavy-socket chisel or the frame chisel.

Two types of metal chisels are required in the electrician's kit. They are the cold chisel and the cape chisel.

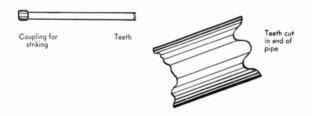

FIG. 6.5. Homemade star drill.

Star Drill. It is necessary for the electrician to have several star drills, for use in drilling holes in concrete, masonry, and similar materials. The star drills (see Fig. 6.5), sizes usually found in the electrician's kit are $\frac{1}{4}''$, $\frac{5}{16}''$, and $\frac{1}{2}''$ sizes.

The **center punch** is used by the electrician to make a small dent or hole for use as a guide in starting his drill. A center punch of medium size will serve all purposes.

Plumb Bob. As in every other construction trade, the plumb bob and line is part of the tool kit of the electrician. The cord is attached to the upper part of the bob, which is used to set up a vertical line for setting boxes, carrying a fixed point down or up vertically.

Files. The electrician frequently finds it necessary to file metal surfaces for cutting or smoothing. His kit should contain three common types of file: the simple flat mill file; the rough file, which is also called the rat tail file, and the half round, or half bastard file.

Rule. The type and size of rule that is used practically everywhere in electrical work, is the 6' folding rule. It is recommended that a strong, sturdy rule of better quality be purchased. It is important that the figures be large and clear, so they can easily be read in dark places.

A **plaster knife** has a broad, flexible blade and is used by the electrician to replaster small holes in walls which must be made in order to reach existing cable or conduit, or to install new ones. For full details of the methods of plastering, the reader is referred to the chapter on this subject in the Masonry book.

Floor Steel. In making additions or repairs in a finished house, it is necessary to cut through the flooring to install or to reach electrical conductors. An excellent tool to use for cutting or "breaking" the tongue in tongue-and-groove flooring is the broad chisel used by plumbers. Electricians however, commonly use a special tool for this purpose, called the floor steel. It consists of a flat piece of thin sheet steel, rectangular in shape, and sharp along one edge. This sharp edge is particularly useful for cutting the tongue along the edges of a section of parquet flooring. In this way the entire section may be removed, thus giving adequate access to the space below the flooring, and making it possible to replace the section of flooring without marring its appearance and finish.

The **snake,** or fish tape as it is sometimes called, is a coil of narrow strip metal which is used for fishing wire or cable through conduit, or through the spaces in the walls and under the flooring of a house. The methods by which this work is done will be described in detail as they arise throughout this book. The snake must be made of a material that is sufficiently flexible to be pushed or pulled around corners and other sharp angles. At the same time, it must be stiff enough so that it is not deflected from its course by minor obstacles, or by the considerable resistance to its passage which results from its rubbing against walls, conduit, and cable.

Alcohol Torch. In electrical work it is most important to have a small portable flame which can produce a fairly high temperature. To produce this flame, electricians use a small alcohol torch, or lineman's torch as illustrated. These torches are commonly arranged with a small pipe which is put in the mouth and used to blow air into the flame as a means of increasing its temperature and directing the flame.

FIG. 6.6. Hickey.   FIG. 6.7. Hickey.

Hand Drill, Twist Drill, Reamers, and Taps. The hand drill is designed to hold steel twist drills, and to rotate them fast enough to cut metal readily. For use in this drill the electrician should have a number of drills of the best quality, in at least these four sizes: #28, #19, #11 and #7. The reamer is used for removing burrs from the inside, cut edges of pipe or rigid conduit, as they result from the cutting operation. The reamer is used in a hand brace. The electrician needs a series of hand taps, corresponding in size to the drill. The hand taps which are used for cutting threads should preferably be of the taper type.

The **hickey** is a practical tool that is commonly used by electricians for bending conduit, without spoiling the true circular cross section of the conduit by kinking or flattening it. A pull on the handle fits the hickey to the conduit with a grip that prevents slipping. Detailed directions for making various bends in conduit will be given in the chapter on conduit.

Hickies are available in a number of types and styles. Among the well known varieties are the Lakin and Henderson models. Hickey sizes correspond to conduit sizes, that is, a $\frac{1}{2}''$ hickey should be used on $\frac{1}{2}''$ conduit; a $\frac{3}{4}''$ hickey on $\frac{3}{4}''$ conduit, etc. See Figs. 6.6 and 6.7.

Spirit Level. Just as the plumb bob and cord are used to make sure the installation is truly vertical, so the spirit level is used to check its accuracy in the horizontal direction.   The spirit level is an important accessory to the electrician's equipment, especially for new installations.

The **awl,** or **brad awl** is used for boring very small holes, and has the advantage that it does not remove the material from the hole it makes and so does not scatter particles of the material bored.   If a brad awl is not available, a sharp ice pick may be used instead.

FIG. 6.8.

The **scriber,** which is also called the scratch awl, has a sharp point, used to draw lines on metal.

Pipe Wrenches.   For assembling or disconnecting rigid conduit, the electrician uses wrenches similar to those used by plumbers in pipe work. Two wrenches large enough to take conduit, or pipe, of 1½″ size, will be found sufficient for all ordinary needs of the electrician.

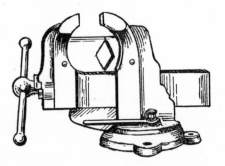

FIG. 6.9.   Combination pipe vise.

The **stock and die** is used by the electrician to thread conduit just as it is used by the plumber to thread pipe.   Figure 6.8 shows the Armstrong type, which has removable dies and collar, and is widely used by electricians. Die sizes are specified by the sizes of the conduit they are used to thread, such as $\frac{1}{2}''$, $\frac{3}{4}''$, $1''$, and $1\frac{1}{4}''$. These sizes just mentioned are the ones most commonly required.

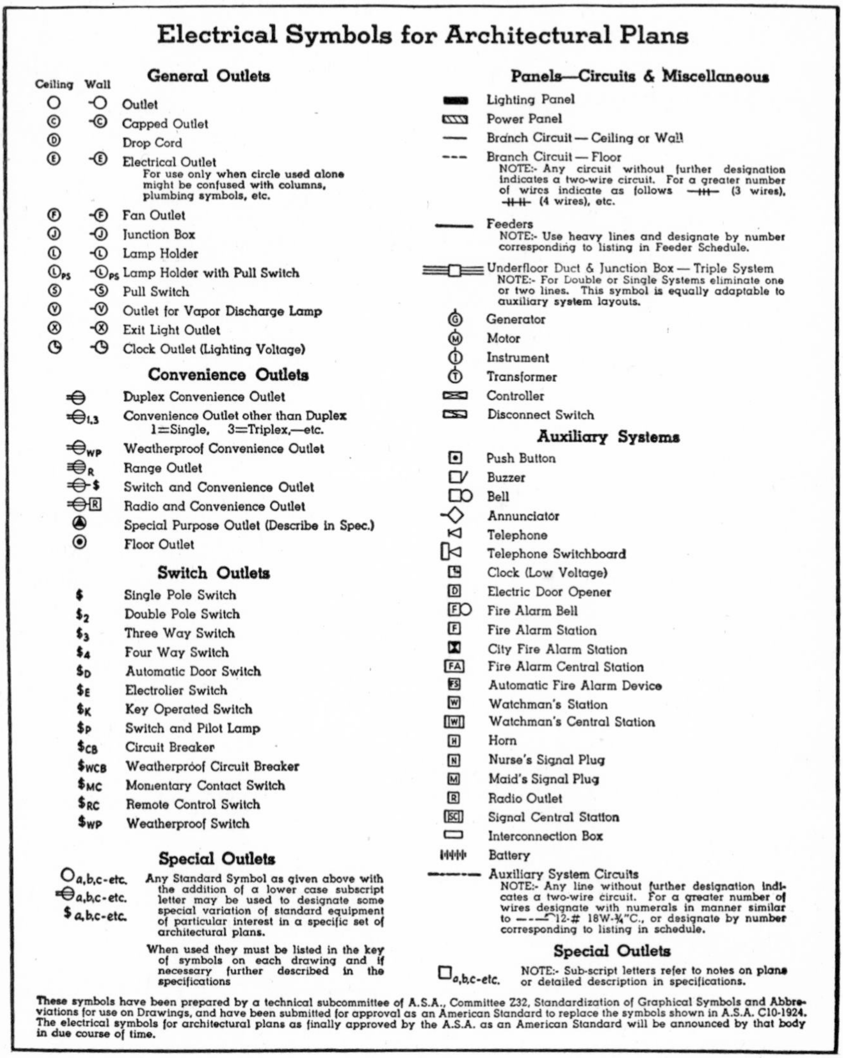

Electrical Symbols for Architectural Plans

General Outlets

Ceiling	Wall	
O	-O	Outlet
Ⓒ	-Ⓒ	Capped Outlet
Ⓓ		Drop Cord
Ⓔ	-Ⓔ	Electrical Outlet

For use only when circle used alone might be confused with columns, plumbing symbols, etc.

Ⓕ	-Ⓕ	Fan Outlet
Ⓙ	-Ⓙ	Junction Box
Ⓛ	-Ⓛ	Lamp Holder
Ⓛ$_{PS}$	-Ⓛ$_{PS}$	Lamp Holder with Pull Switch
Ⓢ	-Ⓢ	Pull Switch
Ⓥ	-Ⓥ	Outlet for Vapor Discharge Lamp
Ⓧ	-Ⓧ	Exit Light Outlet
Ⓒ	-Ⓒ	Clock Outlet (Lighting Voltage)

Convenience Outlets

⊕	Duplex Convenience Outlet
⊕$_{1,3}$	Convenience Outlet other than Duplex 1=Single, 3=Triplex,—etc.
⊕$_{WP}$	Weatherproof Convenience Outlet
⊕$_{R}$	Range Outlet
⊕-$	Switch and Convenience Outlet
⊕Ⓡ	Radio and Convenience Outlet
⊛	Special Purpose Outlet (Describe in Spec.)
⊙	Floor Outlet

Switch Outlets

$	Single Pole Switch
$$_2$	Double Pole Switch
$$_3$	Three Way Switch
$$_4$	Four Way Switch
$$_D$	Automatic Door Switch
$$_E$	Electrolier Switch
$$_K$	Key Operated Switch
$$_P$	Switch and Pilot Lamp
$$_{CB}$	Circuit Breaker
$$_{WCB}$	Weatherproof Circuit Breaker
$$_{MC}$	Momentary Contact Switch
$$_{RC}$	Remote Control Switch
$$_{WP}$	Weatherproof Switch

Special Outlets

O$_{a,b,c-etc.}$	Any Standard Symbol as given above with the addition of a lower case subscript letter may be used to designate some special variation of standard equipment of particular interest in a specific set of architectural plans.
⊕$_{a,b,c-etc.}$	
$ $_{a,b,c-etc.}$	

When used they must be listed in the key of symbols on each drawing and if necessary further described in the specifications

Panels—Circuits & Miscellaneous

▬	Lighting Panel
▨	Power Panel
—	Branch Circuit — Ceiling or Wall
---	Branch Circuit — Floor

NOTE:- Any circuit without further designation indicates a two-wire circuit. For a greater number of wires indicate as follows —⫲⫲— (3 wires), —⫲⫲⫲⫲— (4 wires), etc.

▬▬	Feeders

NOTE:- Use heavy lines and designate by number corresponding to listing in Feeder Schedule.

▤▢▤	Underfloor Duct & Junction Box — Triple System

NOTE:- For Double or Single Systems eliminate one or two lines. This symbol is equally adaptable to auxiliary system layouts.

Ⓖ	Generator
Ⓜ	Motor
Ⓘ	Instrument
Ⓣ	Transformer
⊏⊐	Controller
⊏⊐	Disconnect Switch

Auxiliary Systems

▣	Push Button
▱/	Buzzer
▭	Bell
◇	Annunciator
◁	Telephone
◖◁	Telephone Switchboard
Ⓒ	Clock (Low Voltage)
Ⓓ	Electric Door Opener
Ⓕ◯	Fire Alarm Bell
Ⓕ	Fire Alarm Station
▣	City Fire Alarm Station
FA	Fire Alarm Central Station
▣	Automatic Fire Alarm Device
Ⓦ	Watchman's Station
▣W▣	Watchman's Central Station
Ⓗ	Horn
Ⓝ	Nurse's Signal Plug
Ⓜ	Maid's Signal Plug
Ⓡ	Radio Outlet
▣	Signal Central Station
▭	Interconnection Box
⊪⊪⊪	Battery
––––	Auxiliary System Circuits

NOTE:- Any line without further designation indicates a two-wire circuit. For a greater number of wires designate with numerals in manner similar to —⫲12-# 18W-¾"C., or designate by number corresponding to listing in schedule.

Special Outlets

▢$_{a,b,c-etc.}$	NOTE:- Sub-script letters refer to notes on plans or detailed description in specifications.

These symbols have been prepared by a technical subcommittee of A.S.A., Committee 232, Standardization of Graphical Symbols and Abbreviations for use on Drawings, and have been submitted for approval as an American Standard to replace the symbols shown in A.S.A. C10-1924. The electrical symbols for architectural plans as finally approved by the A.S.A. as an American Standard will be announced by that body in due course of time.

FIG. 6.10.

The **vise** is probably well known but, a few additional facts may be mentioned here, because they apply particularly to vises suitable for conduit work.   Three types of vise are commonly used by electricians.   The combination vise, shown in Fig. 6.9, has a feature which provides for holding conduit or pipe below the main jaws.   A standard-type vise, such as is used by plumbers, is also suitable for electrical work.   The third type, the chain vise, is a convenient portable unit which may be carried around and fastened to a beam, a bench, or any other convenient, rigid article.

Standard electrical symbols are illustrated in Fig. 6.10.

Chapter 3

GENERAL OPERATIONS IN ELECTRICAL WORK

Splicing: Western Union Splice, Tap or Branch Splice, Pigtail Splice, Soldering Splices, How To Splice a Flexible Wire to a Solid Wire — Pigtail Splice, Flexible Cord Splicing, Laying Away Splices ... Fishing ... Conduit Protectors for Bell Wires or BX Cable Passing through Partition Headers and Studs ... Handy Method of Starting a Screw ... How To Test BX Cable Before Installation ... How To Prepare a Set of Test Lamps ... Testing an A.C. Single-Circuit Fuse Block ... Kilowatt Hour Meter ... How To Replace a Male Plug ... How To Terminate a Wire

Splicing.   The need for splicing wires will be found in nearly every electrical job undertaken by the home mechanic.   It is well, therefore, that practice be gained to perfect the simple operations required to make safe and secure splices.   For this purpose it is recommended that several short scrap ends of wire be used, and that each of the three splices, Western Union, Tap Splice, and Pigtail Splice, be practiced until they are made well and easily.

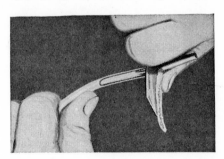

FIG. 6.11.   Skinning a wire.   *Courtesy of General Cable Corporation.*

An excellent formula for good splicing is found in the description offered by every code concerning the regulations on splicing.   This formula is found in the words "Splices must be made electrically and mechanically secure." To make a splice electrically secure, the copper must be thoroughly cleaned before the splice is made, to reduce any resistance to the flow of an electric current which may be caused by the presence of dirt or impurities.

The words "mechanically secure" mean that the splice, when completed, must be firm and tight. To be absolutely certain of this, general practice and code requirements state that all splices be soldered (except signalling wiring under 24 volts; however, it is well to include all splices), and then taped with a covering at least equal to the insulation of the wire. Soldering and taping are covered in this chapter, immediately after splicing. One

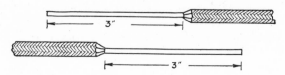

a. Remove 3″ of insulation from both wire ends — clean copper well.

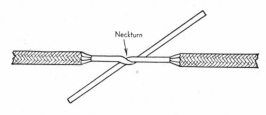

b. Cross skinned wires at a point about ¾″ from insulation and make a neckturn as shown.

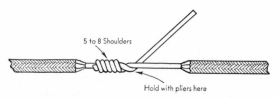

c. Make from 5 to 8 shoulders using thumb and forefinger.

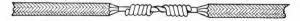

d. Shoulders completed on both sides of neckturns.

FIG. 6.12. How to make a Western Union Splice to lengthen a wire.

point should be constantly kept in mind regarding splicing. It is a violation of every code and every dictate of safe practice to place a splice in conduit, or any other raceway except at accessible outlets and fittings in the installation.

Western Union Splice. Wires must be lengthened for many electrical purposes, and the trade name given to this splice is "Western Union." Both wires to be spliced are first "skinned" (insulation removed) for a distance of approximately 3″ at each free end (see Fig. 6.12). This may be done with a pocketknife (Fig. 6.11). Both bare wires should then be cleaned. The back of a knife blade is best for this purpose. Care should be exercised when using the back of the blade to avoid having the knife close suddenly.

To make the actual splice, cross the two bare wire ends, and make a neck turn as shown in Fig. 6.12b. The cross should be made about ¾″ from the insulation on either wire. Following the neck turn, which prevents the splice from being opened under pulling pressure, a number of shoulders (from five to eight) are made using the thumb and forefinger (Fig. 6.12c). A pair of cutting pliers is used to cut off the excess wire and to tighten the shoulders. Figure 6.12d shows the completed splice ready for soldering.

Tap or Branch Splice. A tap or branch splice is used to make a connection to a main wire. The splice is really one half a Western Union Splice, as can be seen from the operations required to make it. The main wire is skinned a distance of approximately 1″ as shown in Fig. 6.13a. The branch wire end is skinned about 3″, the same as for a Western Union Splice. Figure 6.13b shows how the splice should be started. The branch wire is placed across the main wire, insulation to insulation, and a neck turn made first to ensure against a loose or slipping splice. The neck turn is followed by from five to eight shoulders as shown in Fig. 6.13c. Excess wire may be cut off and the shoulders tightened with a pair of pliers. The splice is then ready for soldering and taping.

Pigtail Splice. The pigtail splice is probably one of the most useful of all electrical splices. It is easily made, and it has the advantage of being easily unmade. This means it is well suited for temporary, as well as permanent, installations. Again, it will hold well (if soldered) when used for splicing solid and stranded wires together.

To make a pigtail splice, prepare the wire ends as shown in Fig. 6.14a. Remove about 2″ of insulation from each wire end and clean the exposed copper surface of the wires. Next, place the wires parallel to each other, insulation to insulation, as shown in Fig. 6.14b. Using a pair of pliers, make a series of twists at least 1″ in length. Cut off excess wire. This splice may be made with more than two wires. Soldering and splicing should follow the completion of the splice.

Soldering Splices. To ensure a mechanically secure splice, that is, one which will not open under ordinary pressure, it is necessary to solder the joint. An alcohol blow torch is generally used for this purpose. It has a rubber hose attachment, through which a blast of air may be directed at

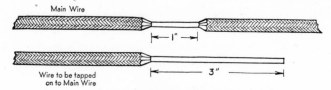

a.   Skin the wires as shown.   Clean copper well.

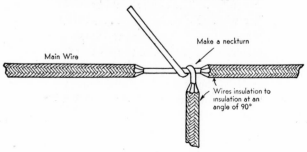

b.   Cross wires and make a neckturn.

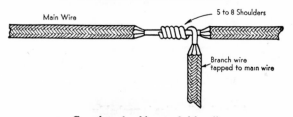

c.   Complete shoulders to finish splice.

Fig. 6.13.   How to make a tap or branch splice.

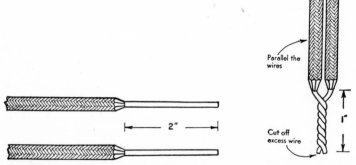

a.   Skin both wires about 2″ from the end.   *b.*   Make twists and com-
Clean well.   plete splice.

Fig. 6.14.   How to make a pigtail splice.

right angles to the torch flame, which in turn will point a flame directly toward the splice to be soldered.

An essential requirement of good soldering is a clean surface. Be sure to remove all dirt, grit, and impurities on the surface of the splice before solder-

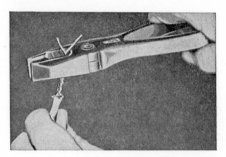

FIG. 6.15. Finishing a pigtail splice (cutting off excess wire).

ing. Then, apply a coat of soldering paste the length of the splice, top and bottom, and around the sides. The best method to ensure a good paste

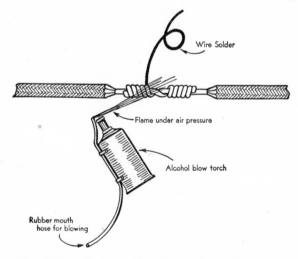

FIG. 6.16. Soldering a splice using an alcohol blow torch.

coating on the splice is to dip the finger into the paste can and apply the paste to the splice by rubbing all surfaces with your finger. Of course, this procedure is unnecessary if rosin-core solder is used.

Following the paste application, direct a flame toward the center of the splice, keeping the flame so directed by blowing air from the mouth through the rubber tube. Allow the metal to heat — evidence of heating will be shown by the paste liquefying and running off the splice. Take a piece of

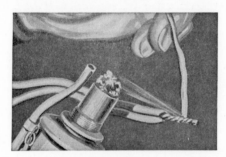

FIG. 6.17. Soldering a splice. *Courtesy of General Cable Corp.*

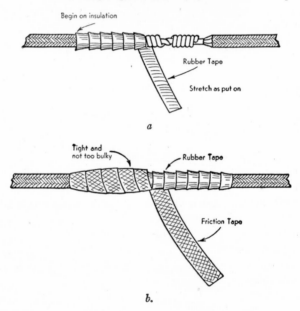

FIG. 6.18. Taping a splice.

wire solder and make contact at the top of the splice. Figures 6.16 and 6.17 show how this should be done. Try several times if necessary until the solder instantly "runs" or "floats" completely through the splice. When this occurs, float solder from one end of the joint to the other. See Fig. 6.19.

How To Splice a Flexible Wire to a Solid Wire — Pigtail Splice. Permanent wiring usually is made with solid conductors. Fixtures and appliances are generally wired with flexible conductors. Frequently it will be found necessary to splice them together — a stranded wire to a solid wire to make a connection.

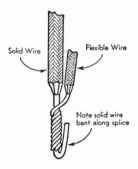

Solid Wire
Flexible Wire
Note solid wire bent along splice

FIG. 6.19. How to splice a flexible wire to a solid wire — pigtail splice.

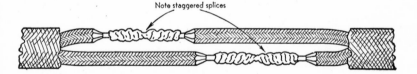

Note staggered splices

FIG. 6.20. Splicing a flexible cord.

Figure 6.19 shows a sketch of a pigtail splice connecting a stranded or flexible conductor to a solid conductor. After the stranded conductor has been wrapped around the solid conductor a number of times the solid conductor is bent parallel to the splice. This bend-back along the splice will provide an excellent solder bed when the splice is later soldered.

Flexible Cord Splicing. Flexible cord or stranded wire, where twin wires are employed in one cord, must often be lengthened. Figure 6.20 shows a sketch of the most important point to remember in making joints in these wires. Splices are staggered, that is, one splice does not begin before the other ends. This method will help to avoid short circuits and accidental contacts between the wires.

Laying Away Splices. Difficulty may be experienced in laying away splices at outlets, switch boxes, and the like due to an apparent lack of space.

A method of overcoming this difficulty is shown in Fig. 6.21. Note that pigtail splices are used because they take up very little space. Note also that splices are pointed in opposite directions to avoid bulking at any one point, and to make use of the available free space in the box.

The same procedure may be used for splices in switch boxes, receptacle outlets and pull boxes (see Fig. 6.22).

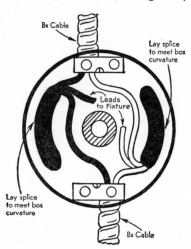

FIG. 6.21. Sketch showing how to lay away splices in a fixture outlet.

FIG. 6.22. *Courtesy of General Electric Co.*

Fishing. Wires are pulled through conduits, BX cables are drawn through partitions, under floors and over hung ceilings by means of a stiff wire snake. The trade term for the operation is *fishing*.

Wires cannot always be pushed by hand through conduit runs. Long runs and runs with opposing bends must be fished. For conduit runs, much of this fishing may be snaked from one end, that is, it is possible to push a snake through a conduit, beginning at one outlet, and experience little or no trouble forcing it out at the other end of the conduit run. The snake is forced through the conduit about 6″ at a time, and a pair of electrician's pliers is used to do the forcing. However, some conduit runs may be fairly long, or may have opposing bends, which will make a free passage of the snake forced from one end very difficult, if not impossible. In this event the usual practice is to fish from both ends of the conduit run, forcing one snake in as far as it will go, then "hooking" it with another snake wire forced in through the opposite end.

Greater difficulties will be encountered in concealed BX cable wiring. No confining area, such as is offered by the smooth inside of a conduit run, will exist to guide the snake on its path. Obstructions will be met, such as building debris in partitions, beams, braces, and joists in ceilings and the like. Most BX cable runs will require fishing from two points.

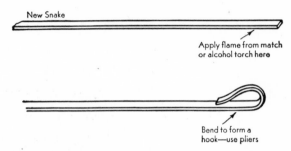

FIG. 6.23. How to make a hook on the end of a snake for fishing and wire pulling through conduits.

Before any fishing is done the snake wire must be properly prepared, if this has not been attended to previously. A hook must be made on the snake wire end, which will provide a smooth, rounded, moving surface to help the snake in its forward progress, and to enable another, similarly prepared snake wire to hook with it when fishing from two directions, and to

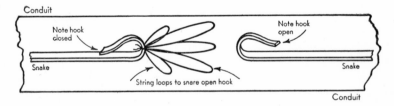

FIG. 6.24. Sketch showing how a long conduit run may be fished from two directions with string loops on one hook to snare the open hook.

provide a means of securing either wires or BX cable to it for drawing it through.

A hook may be made as shown in the two illustrations in Fig. 6.23.

Heat is applied either by a match, an alcohol torch, or a gas stove to prepare the end of the snake wire for bending. When the snake wire reaches a red heat, a hook is bent close to the end with a pair of pliers. When the wire is allowed to cool, it will be found that slight pressure with a pair of pliers will either open or close the hook as desired.

Where a conduit run must be fished from two ends, the following procedure is helpful (see Fig. 6.24).

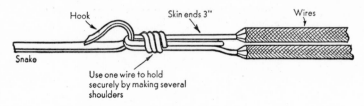

FIG. 6.25.   Sketch showing how to secure wires to snake for fishing.

One snake, with a closed hook, has attached to it several short loops of string.   These loops will provide additional opportunities for the second snake with its open hook to make contact.   When contact is made, one or

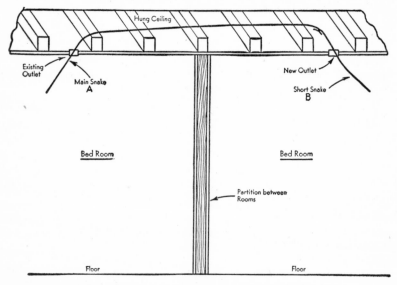

FIG. 6.26.   How to fish through a hung ceiling between rooms.

the other of the two snake wires may be drawn completely through the run, after which the wires are attached and then drawn permanently in place. Wires or BX cable should be attached to a snake wire as shown in Fig. 6.25.

In attaching single wires or a BX cable to a snake, wires should be skinned about 3″ from the free ends to be attached.   All wires are passed through the hook (which should be closed).   One wire is then bent around all the others to form several shoulders, similar to those that would be made in a Western Union Splice.

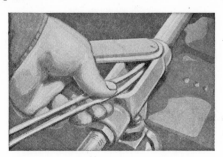

FIG. 6.27.   Feeding wires into a conduit run.

An example of hung ceiling fishing is shown in Fig. 6.26.   Positions of the permanent outlet are determined or already fixed.   An opening is made for the new outlet, and one snake is forced from the existing outlet in the direction of the new outlet.   When the snake has been forced near the new outlet, a second snake is used to fish out the first snake.   Cable may then be attached and drawn into permanent position.

Conduit Protectors for Bell Wires or BX Cable Passing through Partition Headers and Studs.   There is danger of a nail being driven into a header or stud, especially lathing nails, when a BX cable or bell cable is passing through fairly close to the surface of the wood.   Protection may be provided by using a short pipe nipple, long enough to extend a few inches on either side of the wood stud or header, which will form a protective covering sufficiently strong to deflect a nail from it.   Figure 6.28 shows how a pipe nipple may be installed for this purpose.

Handy Method of Starting a Screw.   Considerable trouble may be experienced in trying to hold an electrical device or piece of equipment with one hand and start a screw with the other hand, when securing or connecting.

A handy method which is used for this purpose is shown in Fig. 6.29.   A piece of friction tape about 1″ in length is shaped over the end of the screwdriver as shown.   The screwdriver, with the tape covering, is then inserted into the slotted head of the screw and a little hand pressure applied to keep it in place.   This will permit one-handed operation while inserting the screw in place and assisting the thread to start.

How To Test a BX Cable before Installation.   Occasionally a defective piece of BX cable will unknowingly be installed and, afterwards, trouble will

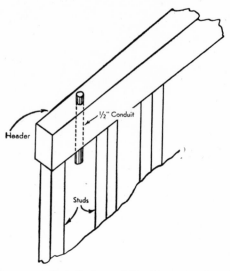

FIG. 6.28.   Conduit protector for bell wires or BX cable passing through partition header.

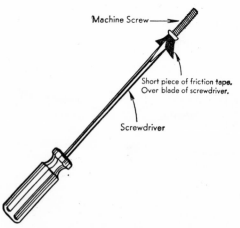

FIG. 6.29.   Handy method of starting a screw.

develop within it.   It is most unpleasant to spend several hours working **and then** discover a defective cable which passed your visual inspection.

To avoid installing defective BX cable, a simple continuity test using a bell and a battery is suggested (see Fig. 6.30). If the cable is all in one piece, so

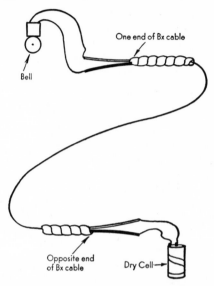

Bell

One end of Bx cable

Opposite end of Bx cable

Dry Cell

FIG. 6.30. How to test a BX cable before installation.

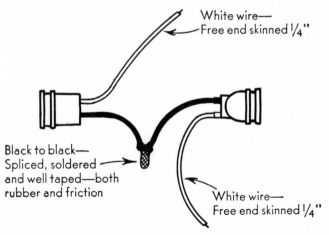

White wire—
Free end skinned 1/4"

Black to black—
Spliced, soldered
and well taped—both
rubber and friction

White wire—
Free end skinned 1/4"

FIG. 6.31. How to prepare a 230 volt set of test sockets.

much the better, for then all of it can be tested at one time. If several pieces are to be used, each piece should be tested separately before it is

installed.   If the bell rings when attached to one end of the cable (a battery
is connected to the other end), the cable is satisfactory.

How To Prepare a Set of Test Lamps.   Frequently there is occasion to test
for a blown fuse or to check on the pressure of live current at an outlet.
Obviously, it is not recommended that finger testing be used, that is,
touching contacts or wires with bare fingers to determine the presence of
electricity.   Such practice is dangerous.

For general testing purposes we may prepare a set of test lamps consisting
of two weatherproof sockets connected in series as shown in Fig. 6.31.
Weatherproof sockets are used because no metal parts are exposed, and this
will reduce the possibility of accidental contact while using the test set.
Lamps of equal wattage, preferably low wattage such as 15 watts, are used.
The low voltage lamps are small in size and easy to handle.

WARNING!!   The following operation is dangerous for anyone who has
not had considerable experience with electrical installation.

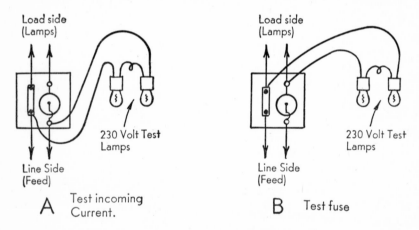

FIG. 6.32.   Testing on A.C. single circuit fuse block.

Testing an A.C. Single-Circuit Fuse Block.   To test for a blown fuse in a single circuit
A.C. cutout block, as shown in Fig. 6.32, first study both sketches thoroughly.   Note the
construction features of an A.C. cutout block.   Only one fuse is used for each circuit.   The
neutral is connected to a strip of solid copper, brass, or similar metal by means of terminal
screws.   The positive wire is broken through the fuse.

In all work near incoming lines (that is, before reaching the house fuses), be sure to
stand on an absolutely dry surface.   This is a rule in all electrical work.

First, make sure that there is incoming current to the block by testing across the
incoming terminals as shown in Fig. 6.32A.   If the test lamps light "half-bright," current

is present there. Next, place the lead from the test lamps which was making contact with the incoming terminal of the fuse on the outgoing or load side of the fuse. If the lamps remain dark the fuse is blown out and should be replaced.

The connections for testing for a blown fuse in a D.C. two-wire cutout block are shown in Fig. 6.33.

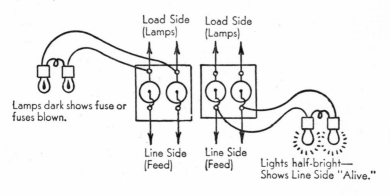

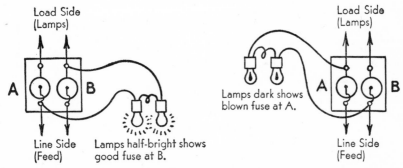

FIG. 6.33. How to test for a blown fuse, D.C. 2-wire cutout block, using test lamps.

Kilowatt Hour Meter. Every home, apartment, or private house using electricity has a kilowatt hour meter which records the electrical power consumed on the premises. In its basic operation a kilowatt hour meter is a combination voltmeter and ammeter.

It is desirable to know how to read a kilowatt hour meter in order to check the consumption of electricity in the home at stated intervals, usually monthly.

Study the reproduction of a kilowatt hour meter dial face shown in Fig. 6.34. Note the arrows over each dial indicating the direction of rotation of each hand. The meter is read from right to left. The dial on the extreme right is the *units* dial and revolves in a clockwise direction. To the left, the second dial is the *tens* dial and, it revolves in a counterclockwise direction. The next dial is the *hundreds* dial, and it revolves in a clockwise direction. Finally, the last dial on the left of the meter is the *thousands* dial and, like the tens dial, revolves in a counterclockwise direction.

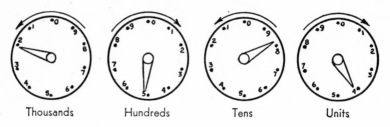

Thousands   Hundreds   Tens   Units

Fig. 6.34.   Reading — 2584 kilowatt-hours.

It will be noted that two dials revolve in a clockwise direction, the units and hundreds dials, and two revolve in a counterclockwise direction, the tens and thousands dials

To read the meter, note the position of the indicator on the units dial. Put down on paper the last number that the units dial or indicator has passed (determined by the dot at the number).   In the illustration the indicator on the units dial reads 4 since it has passed the dot at that point but has not reached the next dot.   The tens indicator has just passed 8, so write the 8 to the left of the 4 as: 84.   Reading the hundreds indicator, it has passed 5 but has not reached the dot at 6.   Consequently, the hundreds reading is 5 and should be written to the left of the previous tens and units figures to get 584.   The thousands indicator is between 2 and 3, and should be read as 2.   Add this to the left of the other figures and obtain a final reading of 2584 kilowatt hours.

Monthly readings may be taken as illustrated, and the difference in kilowatt hours between each monthly reading multiplied by the cost per kilowatt hour will determine the amount of the electric bill.

How To Replace a Male Plug.   Male plugs are used for appliance cords to make contact with the existing house circuit and may be found on the cord end of table and floor lamps, vacuum cleaners, refrigerators, and many other electrical appliances.   Replacing a male plug will be a regular chore for the home mechanic.

Many housewives and others have a habit of removing the plug from the base receptacle by grasping the flexible cord a few feet from the plug and pulling the plug free.   This is a poor practice, which will lead to serious electrical trouble, including a blackening of the wall surface around the receptacle which results from a flash caused by a short circuit, not to mention the possibility of shock or burn to the person removing the plug.

All this may be avoided if the instructions for replacing a male plug given here are followed.   Code regulations are followed carefully in the operations suggested.

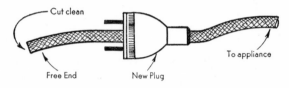

Cut clean

Free End   New Plug

To appliance

FIG. 6.35.   Push plug on wire.

To replace a male plug, begin as shown in Fig. 6.35 by cutting the used end of the appliance cord clean and slipping the new plug over the cord with the prong ends of the plug facing the free end.

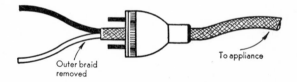

Outer braid
removed

To appliance

FIG. 6.36.   Remove outer braid.

Remove the outer braid or covering as shown in Fig. 6.36.   Care should be exercised to avoid cutting the individual wiring coverings.

To provide protection for the wires against any pulling strain exerted on the attachment cord when separating the plug from a base receptacle, a special knot known as an Underwriter's knot is used.   In Fig. 6.37 the progressive steps in making an Underwriter's knot are shown.   Practice may be had in making this knot by using string or two short wires before making a knot for a plug.

Having completed the Underwriter's knot, draw the male plug over the knot so it will fit snugly into the recess provided in the plug for this purpose, as shown in Fig. 6.38.   Place the wire ends into position as shown in Fig. 6.39 and mark the points where the insulation is to be removed from the wires to make contact with the terminal screws.   It is important to remember that wires should be fastened around terminal screws in the same direction that the terminal screw turns to tighten. This direction is clockwise.

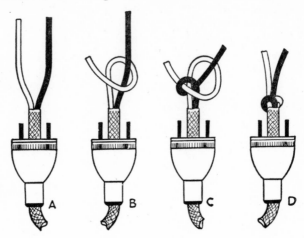

FIG. 6.37. Making Underwriter's knot.

FIG. 6.38. Pull plug over knot.

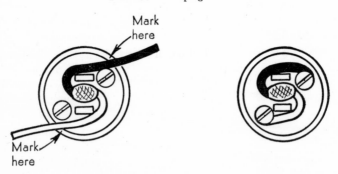

FIG. 6.39. Correct position of wire ends.

FIG. 6.40. Final position of wires.

An alcohol blow torch or light soldering iron should then be used to "tin" the loose wire ends of each wire into a solid wire. This is done by applying soldering paste, after having firmly twisted the separate strands of a conductor together to form a single wire. Apply heat by torch or soldering iron, then use wire solder.

Place the separate wires around the terminal screws as shown in Fig. 6.40, cutting off any excess wire which may extend beyond the terminal screws.

How To Terminate a Wire. Always bear in mind that wires are terminated around terminal screws in the same direction that the terminal screw is

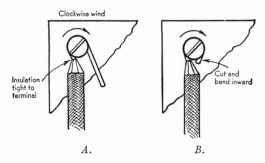

Fig. 6.41. How to terminate a wire.

turned to tighten it. There is a reason for this rule. All terminal screws on switches, sockets, receptacles, and the like tighten in a clockwise direction. If the wire is wrapped around a terminal screw in a counterclockwise direction, tightening the screw will tend to free the wire. This may result in a loose connection or no contact at all.

Fasten a wire to a terminal screw in a clockwise direction. Make certain no bare wire is exposed, by drawing the insulation on the wire up tight to the terminal screw as it is fastened. Cut off all excess wire as closely as possible to the terminal screw.

Chapter 4

SIGNALING SYSTEMS

Apparatus Used in Signaling Systems: Push Buttons, Sources of Supply, Dry Batteries (Dry Cells), Bell Ringing Transformers, Bells, Buzzers, Chimes, Annunciators, Electric Door Opener, Burglar Alarm, Telephones . . . Signaling Circuits: Simple Call Bell Circuit, Front and Rear Door Call System, Return Call Systems, Annunciators, Door-Opener Circuit, Burglar Alarm Circuit, House Telephone Circuit . . . How to Install a Signaling System . . . Testing and Trouble Shooting: To Examine the Source of Supply, To Check the Ringing Equipment, To Investigate the Controlling Device, To Locate an Open Circuit, To Locate a Short Circuit

Signaling systems serve a number of purposes in the home. Entrance doorways are commonly provided with push buttons that ring bells or produce other sounds inside the house. In apartment houses, means are often provided to permit the latch on the front door to be released from each apartment. Burglar alarms, annunciators, and intrahouse telephones are other types of equipment which are operated as parts of signaling systems.

As used by the electrician in reference to house wiring, a signaling system may be defined as a means for transmitting a mechanical signal over an electrical circuit, including the equipment necessary to receive and reproduce the signal. From this definition, it will be seen that every signaling system consists of three essential parts, exclusive of wiring. These parts are (1) a source of electrical current to operate the system, (2) a means of converting the mechanical signal into an electrical current, and (3) a means of reproducing the signal from the electrical current. These parts are briefly described as follows:

1. A *source of supply*, that is, an applied voltage to furnish the current that is needed to operate the system. This applied voltage may be obtained from dry cells or storage batteries, but it cannot be secured by direct connection to the electric power supply from the central station, because signaling systems are operated at low voltages. If, therefore, it is desired to use the regular power supply, the required low voltage must be produced by means of a transformer (on A.C. circuits), or a motor generator set (on D.C. circuits).

2. *Means of Control.* The means used for converting a mechanical signal into an electrical current is called a means of control, because signaling sys-

tems use an electrical controlling device, or switch, as the method of converting a mechanical impulse into an electrical one. For example, pressing the push button with the finger (mechanical action) closes the electrical circuit, thus causing a current to flow (electrical action). Push buttons, keys, and switches, are control devices.

3. *Signaling Equipment.* In the signaling equipment, the electrical current which carries the signal impulse is used to produce a signal that is easily heard or seen. Bells, buzzers, lamps, annunciators, alarms, and telephones are some of the various types of signal equipment. In planning any signal circuit, it is important to remember that the signaling equipment consumes most of the energy used in the circuit.

The discussion of signaling systems in this chapter will be divided into three major sections. The first section will describe at some length the various equipment and control devices used in ordinary signaling systems. A few representative units of this equipment will be illustrated, but the reader is referred, of course, to the manufacturers' catalogs if he wishes to choose styles and types for a particular installation. The second section will explain briefly the circuit diagrams which are used in connecting a number of the more common types of signaling equipment. The third section will show how to use the wiring diagram to install a complete signaling system. The operations will be explained in sufficient detail so that they may be applied to other circuits and systems, to enable the reader to follow the methods given here to accomplish his own installations or repairs.

APPARATUS USED IN SIGNALING SYSTEMS

Push buttons are the most commonly used means of controlling signal systems. Push buttons are simply single-pole switches, consisting essentially of a fixed contact and a movable contact. Pressure against the button causes the movable contact to meet the fixed contact, thus closing the circuit and causing current to flow.

Push buttons may be obtained in a wide variety of sizes and shapes, all of which may be obtained in two commonly used types, surface mounted push buttons, and recessed push buttons (see Figs. 6.42 and 6.43).

Surface mounted push buttons are secured directly to the wall, the trim, or the brick surface beside the door by means of screws. This is done by drilling a hole and installing a wood plug or a Rawl plug. All push buttons are placed at a standard distance of 4' above the finished floor. On plaster walls, surface-type push buttons will hold better and present a neater appearance if mounted upon a wood mat suitably chamfered and finished.

Recessed, or midget push buttons as they are called, are used extensively within a house for room calls, desk calls, etc.   An advantage in using midget push buttons is that they occupy little space and fit flush with the finish, thus cannot easily be seen.

FIG. 6.42.   Surface type
push button. *Courtesy
of Edwards and
Company.*

FIG. 6.43.   Recessed   type
push button (midget).
*Courtesy of Edwards
and Company.*

Push buttons get out of order frequently because of their spring action.   A weakened or spread spring will not make a full surface contact.   In case of trouble with a push button, examine the spring action.

Sources of Supply.   As stated earlier in this chapter, the current used to operate the signal system is obtained from any one of four sources of supply — dry batteries, storage batteries, motor generator sets, or transformers. Storage batteries will be discussed in the chapter which deals with small generating units.   Motor generator sets are limited in their use, for operating signaling systems, chiefly to areas where the power supply is D.C.   Since these areas are so few at the present time, we will not take space necessary to discuss motor generator sets at this point, but will concern ourselves only with dry batteries and transformers.

Dry batteries or *dry cells* are commonly used to furnish current at low voltage for signaling systems.   Figure 6.44 shows the essential parts of a dry cell.   Each dry cell is rated at 1.5 volts to supply a current of about 28 amperes.

To obtain maximum voltage, dry cells should be connected in series.   As explained in Chapter 1, when units are connected in series, the current flowing through each unit (in this case, each cell) is the same as the current that

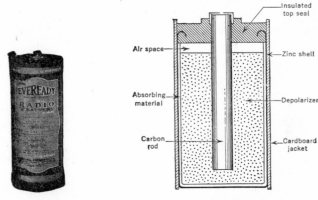

Fig. 6.44A.   Dry cell.   FIG. 6.44B.   Section of dry battery.

flows through the circuit.   The voltage applied to the circuit is, however, the total of the cell voltages.   Thus, with three dry cells connected in series, as shown in Fig. 6.45, the voltage they apply to the circuit is about three times the voltage of one cell, or $3 \times 1.5 = 4.5$ volts.   The current which can be applied to the circuit by the three dry cells connected in series is only that current which can be drawn safely from a single dry cell.

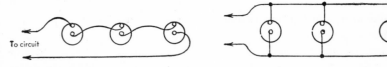

FIG. 6.45.   Dry cells connected in series.   FIG. 6.46.   Dry cells connected in parallel.

To obtain maximum current the dry cells may be connected in parallel, although this connection is rarely used.   As explained in Chapter 1, when units are connected in parallel, the current in the circuit is the total in the currents through the branches, which, in this case, are the batteries.   The voltage applied to the circuit by the three dry cells connected in parallel is only that of a single cell.   Thus, the three dry cells in Fig. 6.46, apply to the circuit only 1.5 volts, although the current they can furnish is three times the value that can safely be drawn from a single cell.

Dry cells should be placed in a cool, dry location, where they will be effective for a longer period of time.

A *bell ringing transformer* is used to step down the voltage of a lighting circuit to the required voltage of the signaling system and its equipment.

Figure 6.47 shows a typical bell ringing transformer. It has a low voltage side, to which the feeder wires for the signaling system are attached (note terminal screws on housing. The heavy leads, one black and one white, are made of standard No. 14 lighting wire and are used to make a connection to the lighting circuit.

Fig. 6.47. Bell-ringing transformer. *Courtesy of Edwards and Company.*

Fig. 6.48. Fused type bell transformer. *Courtesy of Edwards and Company.*

Figure 6.48 shows a fuse protected, bell ringing transformer which can be used in communities where code requirements make it mandatory to fuse separately a bell transformer circuit. These units may be obtained with either single or double fusing and are totally inclosed as an added protection.

Bells are the most widely used of all signaling equipment. They produce a clearly audible signal and may be obtained in many styles and tones. Bells are usually made in one or the other of two operating types: vibrating bells and single-stroke bells. A vibrating bell will ring continuously, as long as the button is pressed, whereas a single-stroke bell will ring only once each time the button is pressed, regardless of how long the button is held down.

Figure 6.49 shows an older style of bell that has excellent durability, but lacks trimness and attractiveness. Figure 6.50 shows a newer style of streamlined door bell, which is suitable for almost any scheme of interior decoration.

Vibrating bells are widely used for general signaling purposes and, because of their continuous ring, are best for ordinary uses. House bell circuits and telephones are examples of the use of vibrating bells. Single-stroke bells are used mainly for fire alarms, office calls, and other series-signaling circuits that are commonly used for "coded ringing," in which numbers are sounded by repeated strokes of the bell.

FIG. 6.49. Old style bell. *Courtesy of Edwards and Company.*

FIG. 6.50. New style bells. Covered (*left*) and open (*right*). *Courtesy of Edwards and Company.*

Bells are usually placed from 5½' to 8' off the finished floor and are mounted with the gongs facing downward, to permit the force of gravity to aid the action of the hammer, and also to prevent dirt accumulation under the housing. Bell sounds may be varied by slotting the bell gong with a hack saw, thus providing a means of distinguishing between calls registered by two or more bells located close together.

Wooden mats may be used to provide an even bed for mounting two or more instruments side by side. Flat head wood screws of sufficient length to hold the mat securely to the wall are used. Sizes No. 6 or No. 8, flat head, iron, wood screws, 1½" long, are commonly used.

A **buzzer** is an audible signaling device which is similar to a bell except there is no hammer or gong. Thus, a buzzing noise is made by the rapid motion of the armature.

Buzzers are made in many sizes and shapes from the midget watch case type used for testing purposes to the general usage utility buzzer shown in Fig. 6.51. In the illustration, the compact arrangement of the internal parts is clearly seen. Buzzers are used for general signaling purposes, where a signal is desired that differs from the sound of a bell, or where a more subdued tone is required.

For attaching buzzers, mounting screw holes are provided within the frame under the cap. Buzzers, like bells, make a better appearance when mounted upon wooden mats. They should be mounted from 5½' to 8' off the finished floor.

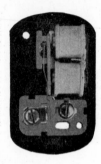

FIG. 6.51. Buzzer (*cover off*). *Courtesy of Edwards and Company.*

FIG. 6.52. Single entrance chime.

FIG. 6.53. Annunciator. *Courtesy of Edwards and Company.*

Chimes. Present day practice among discriminating home owners is to replace the harsh noises of bells and buzzers with the musical notes offered by chimes. Many designs and tones are available at a wide range of prices.

One of the less expensive units is shown in Fig. 6.52. Chimes for single and double entrance calls would replace front and rear door bell and buzzers. Single note chimes and two note single entrance chimes are suitable for front door calls. Two entrance chimes are designed for front and rear call circuits.

An **annunciator** is a unit of signaling equipment which registers several calls, originating at several points. The annunciator must indicate the particular point from which the call comes, and must also produce an audible or visible signal to indicate that a call has been registered. An annunciator consists essentially of a housing in which are mounted a bell or buzzer, a number of drops or indicators electromagnetically controlled, and a means of resetting the drops, either manually or electrically, called a reset.

Figure 6.53 shows a typical six-drop annunciator, surface type, of the less expensive variety. Notice the double-deck windows through which can be seen the indicators as they fall and denote the location of each call.   Annunciators may be obtained with many different numbers of drops each, as: 2, 3, 4, 6, 8, 10, 12, etc.   If an annunciator is not available that has the precise number of drops desired, one with the nearest larger number is used, thus affording a spare for future expansion of the system.

Annunciators may be used in the house to register calls, wherever systems are planned to include more than two calls, that is, other calls besides those from the front and rear doors.   An annunciator located in a kitchen can be used to indicate calls from such locations as the dining room, and individual bed rooms, in addition to the usual front and rear door calls.

Annunciators are used in elevators to indicate calls from different floors. In this case the annunciator is located in the elevator cab and connected to the circuits by means of a flexible traveling cable which rides up and down with the cab.

As stated above, annunciators are usually equipped with a bell or buzzer, which sounds when a call actuates one of the drops.   Lamp annunciators are available where visual instead of audible signals are desired.

Annunciators are usually mounted with the window at about eye level, between 5′ and 5½′ from the finished floor.

An **electric door opener** is shown in Fig. 6.54.   The usual practice is to control the door opener by means of a push button located in the kitchen. When entrance is desired, a front door button is pressed which indicates the call by sounding a bell or buzzer in the kitchen.   Pressing the button in the kitchen which controls the door opener causes the lock to release, thus permitting the front door to be opened.   Door openers are electromagnetically released.   They are mounted in a recess in the door buck.

Burglar Alarm.   Protective systems are important especially in outlying districts.   In addition to the house, chicken coops and pigeon coops may be protected against intruders.   Among the equipment commonly used in burglar alarm systems are springs and traps, relays, and constant-ringing attachments.

Springs for windows, doors, transoms, etc., are shown in Fig. 6.55.   In operation they are similar to single-pole switches and are made with spring action mechanisms.   Window springs are usually mounted in the window frame about 4″ above the lower end of the upper sash and about the same distance below the upper end of the lower sash.   Springs are mortised to fit snug and flush.   Door springs are usually mounted high, to make interference with their operation difficult.

The trap shown in Fig. 6.56 is a small constant-ringing alarm, in principle, which is actuated by means of a mechanical pull such as would be exerted by a string. It is designed for use in tripping circuits, that is, for closing or opening the circuit and so causing a relay to act, by either starting or stop-

FIG. 6.54. Door opener. *Courtesy of Edwards and Company.*

FIG. 6.55. Window spring (*left*) and door spring (*right*). *Courtesy of Edwards and Company.*

FIG. 6.56. Traps. *Courtesy of Edwards and Company*

FIG. 6.57. Relay. *Courtesy of Edwards and Company.*

FIG. 6.58. Constant ringing drop. *Courtesy of Edwards and Company.*

FIG. 6.59. Surface wall telephone. *Courtesy of Edwards and Company.*

ping its primary current, depending upon its arrangement. The relay will usually be set so that its action closes another circuit containing the alarm.

Figure 6.57 shows a commonly used relay of the surface mounting type. Relays are used for open and closed circuit alarm systems.

A unit of equipment called a constant-ringing attachment, or CRA, is used in many alarm circuits. Figure 6.58 shows a typical CRA. It has three connecting terminals and is electromagnetically operated.

Telephones are used for communication purposes. Two general types of instruments are available for small home use, surface and flush. Surface-type instruments are best for after-construction installations, since by their use excessive cutting and patching may be avoided. Flush-type phones are generally more expensive and have a better appearance.

Care should be exercised to see that telephones are not located in the way of swinging doors or passing persons. They should be located in accessible places, not only for convenience in use, but for possible inspection in the event trouble develops with the phone. Telephones should not be located over radiators or near steam pipes or damp walls (Fig. 6.59).

SIGNALING CIRCUITS

In the foregoing section, some of the more common types of signaling circuit apparatus were described, including representatives of each of the three essential, functional elements: sources of supply, means of control, and signaling equipment. In this section a discussion will be given of how these elements of equipment are assembled into workable circuits, leaving for the next section the procedure to be followed in the actual installation of one of these circuits.

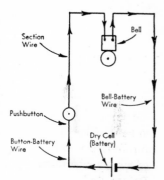

In assembling equipment for a signaling system, careful planning is most important. The plan should take the form of a circuit diagram, which is the essential preliminary to the actual wiring. A properly laid out circuit diagram ensures an electrically correct circuit. In order to familiarize the home owner or home mechanic with properly made circuit diagrams, a few representative diagrams for commonly used signaling equipment will be discussed in the following paragraphs.

FIG. 6.60. Simple call-bell circuit.

Simple Call Bell Circuit. The simplest form of a signal circuit is shown in Fig. 6.60. Note that it consists of a source of supply (battery), ringing equipment (bell), and a means of control (push button). This circuit may be used for a front door call, a sick room call or, in fact, anywhere that a call from one point to another is required.

Note in Fig. 6.60 that, when the push button is pressed closing tne circuit, current will flow from the positive terminal of the source of supply through the *button-battery wire* to the push button; from the push button through the *section wire* to the bell; and from the bell through the *bell-battery wire* to the negative terminal of the source of supply.   Three important terms in the wiring of a signal circuit were introduced here:

1. Button-battery wire
2. Section wire
3. Bell-battery wire

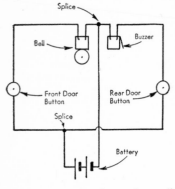

FIG. 6.61.   Front and rear door call system.

Front and Rear Door Call System. Figure 6.61 shows a wiring diagram for a front and rear door call system.   This circuit may be used in a private house where it is necessary to distinguish between front and rear door calls.   A buzzer is, as previously explained, a bell without a hammer and a gong; thus a buzzing, instead of a ringing noise, is produced.

The bell will indicate calls from the front door, and the buzzer, calls from the rear door.   A combination bell and buzzer made in a single unit can be purchased which is more attractive and serves the same purpose as a bell and a buzzer.   The circuit shown in Fig. 6.61 may also be used in apartment houses.   In that event, the bell call would be controlled from the apartment house vestibule, while the buzzer call would be used for a dumbwaiter signal.   This circuit has many applications.

Return Call Systems.   Frequently a call and answer system will be required.   The home mechanic may have his workshop in the basement, in a garage, or in a barn, and want to be called by, or call, the house.   Return call systems are appropriate for this use, in addition to providing the ringing circuit for telephone systems and the wiring for door-opener circuits.

There are two kinds of return call systems which may be installed, each with specific advantages.

Figure 6.62 shows a diagram of a 4-wire return call system.   The term 4-wire is used because four wires are required between stations.   The advantage in using the 4-wire system is that the source of supply may be tapped at either station for additional circuits, since leads connecting directly to the positive and negative terminals of the battery are available at both stations — that is, at both the house end and the workshop end of the circuit.

Figure 6.63 shows a diagram of a 3-wire return call system. The term 3-wire is used because three wires are required between stations. This system has the advantage over the 4-wire system that one wire between

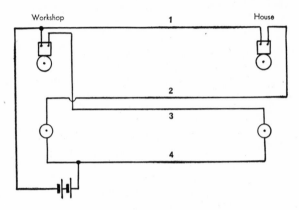

Fig. 6.62. 4-wire return call system.

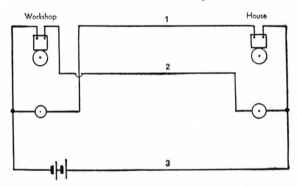

Fig. 6.63. 3-wire return call system.

stations is saved. However, there is also a serious disadvantage, in that a source of supply for additional circuits is only available at one station — the station where the source of supply is located. No additional circuit may be connected to the leads at the other station.

Figure 6.64 shows by diagram how it is possible to design a return call system that uses only two leads between stations. This is accomplished by grounding the circuit at two properly selected points, one in each of the stations. Note that a section of wire from button A is connected to the nearest cold water pipe. Another pick-up from a cold water pipe near the location of bell A is made and connected to bell A as shown. Grounding in signal work, however, is not desirable. It is used frequently to make temporary repairs, until broken or damaged wires can be located and repaired permanently.

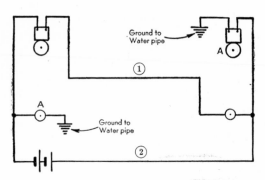

Fig. 6.64.   2-wire grounded return call system.

Annunciators. An annunciator is used where it is necessary to register more than one call using a single bell, and at the same time to make known the location of each call.

Figure 6.65 shows the basic internal wiring diagram of an annunciator.

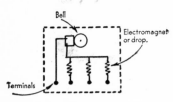

Fig. 6.65.   Internal wiring of an annunciator.

The interior consists of a bell, several drops or indicators each operated by an electromagnet, and a reset for returning the drops to their normal positions after each call. The moving part or drop has a holder to insert a number which will indicate the location of the call. Each drop is in series with the bell, so the bell will ring when any single drop is released by pressing the button which controls it.

An annunciator may be installed in a kitchen to register calls from various parts of the house. A typical annunciator circuit is shown in Fig. 6.66.

Door–Opener Circuit. Figure 6.67 shows a typical door-opener circuit. It will be noted that a 4-wire system is employed. One wire could be saved, by the same method as that described for Return Call Systems, and with the same disadvantages.

Door-opener circuits are used in apartment houses to permit the front door lock to be released by pushing the button located in any apartment. The circuit given here shows merely the connections, both door-bell and door-opener, for a single apartment, but the circuits used in multi-family houses are simply multiple units of this circuit.

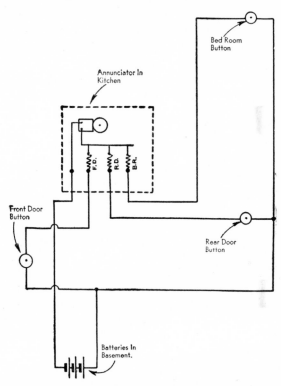

FIG. 6.66.   Annunciator call system — 3 stations.

Burglar Alarm Circuit.   A protective circuit suitable for a barn, chicken coop, or basement windows and door is shown in Fig. 6.68.   In this circuit, a set of batteries is used as the source of supply.   The other equipment in the circuit consists of several springs for installation in doors or windows, a constant ringing attachment, or CRA, and an alarm bell.

This circuit is operated by the opening of a door or window, which releases one or more springs, thus causing current to flow through the CRA.   Since the CRA is in its operation essentially a relay, this flow of current through it brings a secondary circuit into action.   This secondary circuit places the alarm bell directly across the line where it will remain, ringing, until the CRA is reset, or the batteries are exhausted.

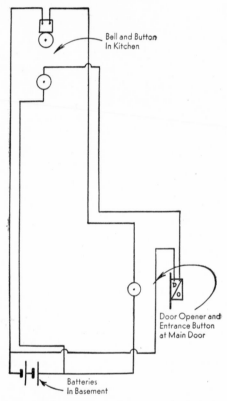

Bell and Button In Kitchen

Door Opener and Entrance Button at Main Door

Batteries In Basement

FIG. 6.67.   Door-opener circuit.

House Telephone Circuit.   House telephone systems are useful in the home to provide a means of communication between any two points. Phones may be installed upstairs and downstairs, or in house and garage, or in house and barn, or in any other two points on the premises.

Figure 6.69 shows the wiring diagram for a simple two-station telephone circuit, in which a common source of supply (batteries) is used to supply the current both for ringing the bells and for carrying the conversations.   When these house telephones systems are purchased, there will usually be found a wiring diagram that has been furnished by the manufacturer.   It is generally pasted on the inside cover of one of the telephone boxes.

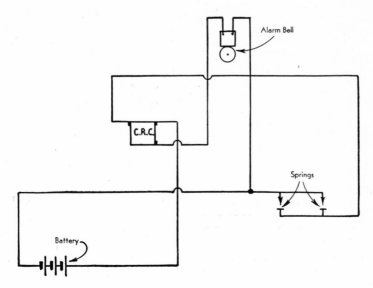

FIG. 6.68.   Open circuit burglar alarm system.

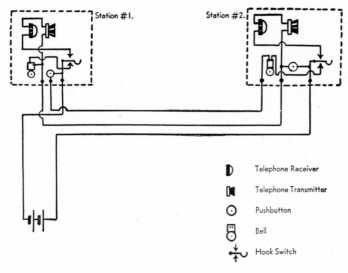

FIG. 6.69.   Two station telephone circuit — 3 wires between stations.

HOW TO INSTALL A SIGNALING SYSTEM

This section will describe the installation of a front and rear call system for use in a one family house of average size.   The various steps in the work will be treated in sufficient detail to enable the reader to modify them to fit the requirements and measurements of his house, as well as to permit him to install other systems than this particular one.

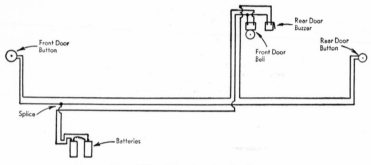

FIG. 6.70.   Planning the circuit.

Whatever system is to be installed, the first step is to plan the circuit in the form of a wiring diagram, so as to ensure satisfactory electrical operation.   This diagram should show not only the apparatus and connecting wires, but also the relative positions of the apparatus.   This does not require an accurate scale drawing, but rather a fairly well proportioned sketch, as shown for this particular installation in Fig. 6.70.   (Comparison of Fig. 6.70 with Fig. 6.72, which is an elevation showing the installation in place in the house, will indicate what is meant by a well-proportioned sketch.)

The front and rear call system to be installed requires the following apparatus: one front door push button, one rear door push button, one bell that is operated by the front door push button, one buzzer that is operated by the rear door push button, and a source of voltage to produce current to operate the circuit.   In this case, the source of supply will be two dry cells which, when connected in series, have an e.m.f. of about 3 volts, which is sufficient to operate a bell or buzzer.   (For the meaning of series connection, see Chapter 1.)   This apparatus should be obtained from a supply house or large hardware store, and its location in the house should be decided.   The positions of the two push buttons are, of course, beside the front and rear doors, at a distance of 4' from the floor.   The bell and the buzzer are to be placed in the kitchen at a point well up the wall.   The batteries are to be located in the basement, at a point close to the front of the house. (This location is chosen for the source of supply because the electric light and power lines usually enter the house at the front and, if this source is used to supply the signaling system, then the bell transformer should be placed close to the point of entrance.)

Before starting the wiring job, it is always advisable to study the wiring diagram carefully. From Fig. 6.70, it will be seen that the wiring can be analyzed and found to consist of the following elements: The two batteries are connected in series (see Chapter 1) by means of a short lead from the positive side of one battery to the negative binding post of the other. This leaves the two batteries connected with two outer binding posts available for connection into the circuit. From one of these battery binding posts, a wire runs out and connects by the splice marked in the diagram to a wire running to both push buttons. Another wire runs from the other battery binding post to the bell and buzzer in the kitchen. A third wire runs from the front door push button to the bell in the kitchen, and a fourth wire runs from the rear door push button to the buzzer in the kitchen.

Now the most obvious method of installation would be to measure the distances covered by each of these wires, to cut pieces of wire of the proper length, and to install and connect them one by one. The method that is widely used by electricians, however, is to prepare all the wiring before commencing installation, and then to put it in place, making all the connections at one time. This method usually saves much time and labor. It will be described here, for use on this particular job, in a way that has been made slightly longer and more detailed than would be used by the electrician, in order to help the man who is doing it for the first time.

The essential feature of the method used by electricians is to set up a series of fixed points, in some conveniently accessible place, that correspond to the positions of the push buttons, batteries, bell, and buzzer. This can be done, for example, by making the necessary measurements, as indicated by the positions of the apparatus as shown in Fig. 6.70 or Fig. 6.72; then, by driving nails into the sheathing on the outside of the house in accordance with these measurements; and by laying out and cutting the various wires as determined by the positions of the nails. For the particular job being done, we proceed in the following way.

First find the overall length of the wires or cable. (The term cable is used here to mean two or more wires which are run together and held together by a protective casing which on this job will be merely tape.) By measurement, find that the house is 22' long, and that the distances from the position

of the cable on the basement ceiling to the positions of the front door push
button and the rear door push button are both 6′.   Therefore, the overall
length of wires running from front door push button to rear door push button
will be 22′ + 6′ + 6′ = 34′.   Take a roll of No. 18 bell wire, wrap one end
lightly around Nail 1 (allowing about 1′ wrap for making connection), and
run the wire to Nail 2, pulling it straight and level.   At Nail 2 cut the wire,
leaving enough excess to wrap lightly around the nail.   The 34′ length of
wire just cut will be found in the wiring diagram (Fig. 6.70), connecting the
front door push button with the rear door push button.

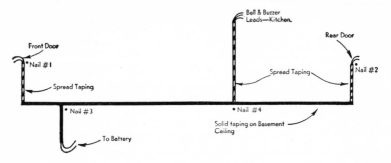

Fig. 6.71.   Making up the cable.

As this wire is traced on the diagram, find a splice where it is joined by a
lead from the battery.   The position of this splice determines the position of
Nail 3.   Since this splice is 4′ from the front wall, along the cable, and since
the front door bell is 6′ above the position of the cable on the basement ceiling, put Nail 3 a distance of 4′ + 6′ = 10′ from Nail 1.   Now cut the short
lead from the battery to the splice on the cable.   Its length is determined by
the distance from one of the available binding posts on the battery to the
position of the cable on the basement ceiling and is found by measurement to
be 3′.   After cutting this length of wire, twist one end of it lightly around the
34′ lead that is to run from push button to push button at the point where
that lead passes Nail 3.   This is the splice point that is to be soldered later.
The free end of this 3′ battery lead is the point from which the wire from
battery to bell and buzzer is started.   Before cutting that wire, however,
put Nail 4 in place.

By reference to Figs. 6.71 and 6.72, it will be seen that the distance of Nail
4 from Nail 2 can be found by adding the distance from rear door push button
down to the position of the cable on the basement ceiling, which has been
found to be 6′, to the distance of the kitchen partition from the rear outside

wall, which by measurement is 8'. Therefore, drive Nail 4 at a distance of $6' + 8' = 14'$ from Nail 2.

Now, return to the wire from battery to bell and buzzer. Twist the end of the coil of wire around the end of the battery lead, which extends, as cut above, 3' out from Nail 3. Then run the battery lead from this point 3' out from Nail 3, to Nail 3, then to Nail 4, and finally to a point out from Nail 4 a distance equal to the height of bell and buzzer on the kitchen wall above the

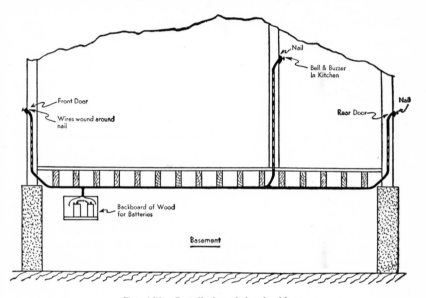

FIG. 6.72.   Installation of signal cable.

position of the cable on the basement ceiling. This distance above or out from Nail 4 has been found by measurement to be 9'. At this point cut the wire and place a knot in it to show that it is the battery lead.

Now install the section of wire from the front door button to the kitchen bell. This wire is wrapped around Nail 1 as before, to start, then run parallel with the other wires to the Nail 4, where a turn is taken for anchorage and an additional 9' of wire (same as the other lead at this point) is measured, before cutting off the wire.

The last wire to be cut is the section wire that runs from the button at the rear door to the kitchen buzzer. Starting in the usual manner, by anchoring it at Nail 2, a wire is run to Nail 4, made fast at that point, and an additional 9' measured off before cutting.

At this time, it is well to stop the other work, in order to make the tap splice for the battery connection. It will be recalled that the battery lead was left twisted about the bell-buzzer lead at the point where this splice was to be made. Now this splice should be made and soldered (as described in Chapter 3) and thoroughly taped to cover all bare wires.

The cable is now ready for taping. Two methods of taping are to be employed. Spread taping is used where the cable is to be concealed in partitions, and solid taping where the cable is to be exposed on the basement ceiling. Starting at a point 1′ from the end of the cable which is to be connected to the front door button (Nail 1), spread tape the wires for a distance of about 6′. Do the same at the rear door button end (i.e., 1′ from Nail 2). At the kitchen tap-off (Nail 4), spread tape from the main line to within 1′ of the wire ends. Do the same thing at the battery tap-off. All the remaining sections of the cable should then be solid taped. The cable is now ready for installation and may be rolled in a loop (fairly large) for ease in carrying.

Figure 6.72 shows the cable in place. The first step in the actual installation of the cable is to provide anchorages at the front door buck, the rear door buck, and the kitchen. This is done by driving nails at the approximate locations. Holes are then bored to the open basement under each location. A brace and wood bit may be used for this purpose. The bit should be large enough to permit free passage of the cable. A ½″ bit is a good size to use. The cable may then be installed as shown and secured in place against the basement ceiling with insulated staples. Wire ends (not to exceed 16″) are wrapped around nail anchors at each location.

Usually this installation will be made in new houses when they are in the "lath" stage, that is, when framing, studding, and partitions are in place. In that case, the fixtures are not installed until the outside and roof of the house have been made permanent, and until the walls have been plastered. Bell and buzzer should be mounted on a neat wooden mat, and the mat fastened to the wall at the desired location, from 5½′ to 8′ off the finished floor. Remember that the wire end with the knot is the battery lead for bell and buzzer. This wire should be connected to one terminal of both the bell and the buzzer. This may be done by "looping," that is, skinning 1″ of the wire about 5″ from its end, just enough to wrap around a terminal, and continuing the lead to the second instrument. This method avoids a splice. Two of the 9′ lengths of wire that extended at Nail 4 should be left, one for the bell and the other for the buzzer. If they are displaced by error, later testing will determine whether it is necessary to reverse them.

Push buttons may now be installed at both front and rear doors, and the wires attached. This will leave only the batteries to be installed in the basement, and the system should be ready for operation. It is advisable to make a box of wood to enclose the batteries as an added protection.

Signaling systems in operation will get out of working order frequently, and the home mechanic will find it useful to know the standard practices employed by the electrician to locate trouble. Before checking the wiring there are three points in any signal circuit where trouble should be sought. These points are the source of supply, the signal equipment, and the means of control.

To Examine the Source of Supply. The most likely place where trouble will start in any electrical circuit is the source of supply. Test the batteries or transformer (low voltage side), either with a bell or a voltmeter. Dry cells can be tested by *tonguing*, that is by placing your tongue across the terminals. A strong salt taste will result if there is any life left in the battery. *Sparking* is another method. Use a short piece of wire and touch both terminals quickly. If a good spark results, the cell is in working condition.

To Check the Ringing Equipment. If the battery is in working order, remove one dry cell and attach two leads to it. Go to the bell or buzzer and temporarily attach the dry cell to the bell terminals. Often a slight adjustment of the vibrator will restore a bell or buzzer to operation. The reason for this is that bell troubles begin with moving parts. The hammer may bend out of shape and not strike the bell gong fairly. In this case, slight pressure with the fingers will restore the hammer to its normal operating position. The armature spring may be frozen against the contact point or, through long operation, it may have become separated too far from the contact point. In either case, finger pressure on the spring near a point when the spring is attached to the armature will usually restore it to normal operation.

To Investigate the Controlling Device. If the source of supply and the ringing equipment are found to be in good working order, short-circuit the button by bridging the two wires at the button with the blade of a pocket knife. Often the metal contacts in a button fail to function, and this trouble can be discovered by this method. If the bell rings when the knife blade is applied, the trouble may be located in the button.

Two common troubles are encountered in the wiring of signaling circuits.

The first trouble is that a wire may become broken and cause an open circuit. Another common trouble occurs when insulation on two wires is bruised, so that the bare copper wires come into contact.   This is called a short circuit.

To Locate an Open Circuit.   After the three tests described above have been made without result, it will be necessary to examine the wiring.   Check exposed places first, especially any point in the basement and attic (if used for the wiring).   Frequently a break can be detected.   If the front door bell rings in a front and rear door call system, and the buzzer does not, then the wires leading to the rear door should be examined.   When the break is located, a well taped splice should put the system back into operation.

To Locate a Short Circuit.   A short circuit will generally be indicated by trouble at the source of supply, such as rapid consumption of the batteries, or overheating of a transformer.   A short circuit will be indicated if one of the wires which connect to the battery can be used, when disconnected from the battery, to spark a set of good cells connected to the other battery wire. No permanent connections should be made to the battery until the short circuit is located and removed.

Chapter 5

ELECTRICAL WIRING WITH BX CABLE

Code Requirements ... Cutting and Removing Armor ... BX Cable ... BX Connectors ... Outlet Boxes ... Ceiling Boxes ... BX Cable Boxes ... BX Cable Staples ... Ackerman-Johnson Expansive Screw Anchors ... Installing a Base Receptacle Outlet in a Finished Bedroom

BX cable is a trade name for flexible metal conduit carrying insulated wires. Its size (cross-sectional area) depends upon the size of the wires and their number (usually two or three). Further details about BX cable, and the various fittings and other equipment used with it, will be given later in this chapter. Here we are concerned with the advantages and limitations of this type of installation.

BX cable wiring is perhaps the most convenient form of electrical installation for lighting purposes — it is comparatively easy to put into place, and it offers considerable protection to the wires. It is very widely used in new or old houses, for both concealed or exposed wiring, although certain codes, including that of New York City, ban its use for exposed wiring. The matter of code restrictions should, of course, be given first consideration in determining any method of electrical installation. The code that is in force in the place where the work is done should always be observed. The provisions of the National Electrical Code should be followed in all localities which do not, like New York City, have a stricter code of their own. We will, therefore, explain some of the general requirements for BX installation of the National Electric Code, because they are important, not only to satisfy code requirements, but for the safety of the installation and the home itself.

Code Requirements. Under the National Electrical Code, armored cable (type AC) may be used for both exposed work and concealed work in dry locations. Armored cable shall contain lead covered conductors (type ACL) if used where exposed to the weather, or to continuous moisture, or for underground runs. Armored cable shall be secured by approved staples, straps, or similar fittings, so designed and installed as not to injure the cable. Cables shall be secured at intervals not exceeding 4½′, and within 12″ from every outlet box or fitting, except where cable is fished, and except lengths of not over 24″ at terminals where flexibility is necessary.

63

The National Electrical Code further states that exposed runs of cable shall closely follow the surface of the building finish or of running boards, except in the case of lengths of not more than 24″ at terminals, where flexibility is necessary.   It may be installed, for example, in accessible attics and roof spaces, and on the underside of floor joists in basements, where sup-

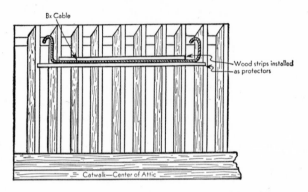

FIG. 6.73.   Protecting a BX cable run on top of floor joists.

ported at each joist, and so located as not to be subject to mechanical injury.

In accessible attics, cable shall be installed as follows: If run across the top of floor joists, or within 7′ of floor or floor joist across the face of rafters or studding, the cable shall be protected by substantial guard-strips

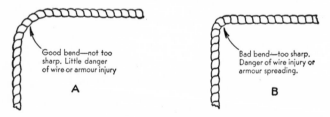

FIG. 6.74.   (A) Correct method of bending BX cable.   (B) Incorrect method.

which are at least as high as the cable (Fig. 6.73). If the attic is not accessible by permanent stairs or ladders, protection will only be required within 6′ of the nearest edge of scuttle hole or attic entrance.

Bends in cable shall be so made, and other handling shall be such, that the protective coverings of the cable will not be injured, and no bend shall have a radius less than five times the diameter of the cable (Fig. 6.74).

In regard to practices in wiring with BX cable, the National Electrical Code provides that outlet boxes or fittings shall be installed at all outlets and switch points.   Boxes used to enclose flush devices shall be of such design

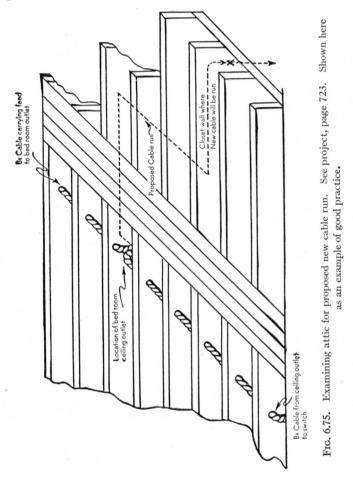

FIG. 6.75.   Examining attic for proposed new cable run.   See project, page 723.   Shown here as an example of good practice.

that the devices will be completely enclosed on back and sides, and that substantial support for the devices will be provided.

In completed installations each outlet box shall be provided with a cover unless a fixture canopy is used.   If a fixture canopy is used any combustible wall or ceiling finish exposed between the edge of the canopy and the outlet box shall be covered with noncombustible material.

In concealed work, outlet boxes and fittings, unless securely held in place by concrete, masonry, or other building material in which they are imbedded, shall be secured to a stud, joist, or similar fixed structural unit, or to a metal

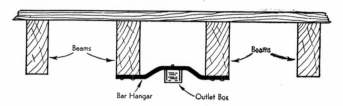

FIG. 6.76. Method of securing an outlet box to beams using a bar hanger BX box.

or wooden support which is secured to such a structural unit. Wooden supports shall not be less than $7/8''$ in thickness (Fig. 6.76).

In walls or ceilings of concrete, tile, or other noncombustible material, boxes, fittings, and cabinets shall be so installed that the front edge of the box

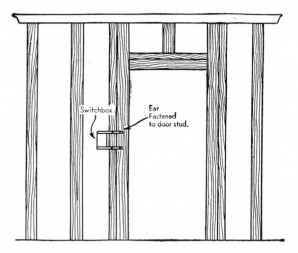

FIG. 6.77. Method of fastening an extended ear switch box to a stud. Same method may be used for receptacles and side wall brackets.

or fitting will not set back of the finished surface more than $1/4''$. In walls and ceilings constructed of wood or other combustible material, outlet boxes, fittings, and cabinets shall be flush with the finished surface or project there-from. Except on walls or ceilings of concrete, tile, or other noncombustible material, a plaster surface which is broken or incomplete shall be repaired so that there will be no gaps or open spaces at the edge of the box or fitting.

Junction boxes shall be so installed that the wiring contained in them may be rendered accessible without removing any part of the building.

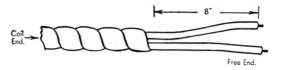

FIG. 6.78. Correct amount of wire beyond armor.

Cutting and Removing Armor. In cutting armored cable for installation, it should always be remembered that standard practice requires about 8" of free wire beyond the armor for splicing and connecting purposes (see Fig. 6.78). This 8" should be allowed at both ends of all lengths of armor that are cut to measurements. Methods of cutting armored cable, and of removing the armor to free the wires for splicing, are described in the following paragraphs.

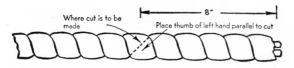

FIG. 6.79. Determining position of cut.

A convenient way to cut armor is by the use of a hack saw. Determine the segment of armor in which the cut is to be made, and hold the cable in the left hand so that the thumb is parallel to the proposed cut, which should be made at an angle of 45° to the lay (see Fig. 6.79). Now, with a hack saw held in the right hand, make a nick along the line to be cut, using short even strokes until you can barely see the space inside the armor. Guide the blade of the hack saw against the left thumb *carefully*, as shown in Fig. 6.80. After nicking the armor lightly from edge to edge of the lay, grasp the armor with both hands and bend it up and down until it breaks. This opens one side of the cable. The under side is then broken by pulling, using a twisting motion as the pulling pressure is applied. This completes the break, freeing the armor. Then, if the wires are to be cut also, this can of course be done with pliers. If, on the other hand, the 8" length of wires is to be freed for splicing, as shown in Fig. 6.79, simply slip off the 8" section of armor. However, before any splicing is done, be sure to insert an anti-short (a small fiber bushing described later in this chapter) between the armor and the wires to prevent accidental grounds and shorts.

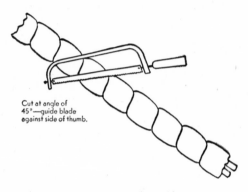

Cut at angle of
45°—guide blade
against side of thumb.

FIG. 6.80.   Cutting cable.

BX Cable may be obtained with wires of standard sizes, and either two or three of them in the cable. All conductors are designated by the colors of their insulation, which are standard colors. A two-wire BX cable includes one white insulated wire and one black insulated wire. See Fig. 6.81. A three-wire BX cable includes one white, one black, and one red insulated wire. Colors are used for identification purposes. The white wire, or a wire with a white tracer, is always used as a neutral wire. The black wire is commonly used for the "hot leg" (live wire) and the red for switch control.

FIG. 6.81.   BX cable.

BX Connectors. BX cable must be terminated at all outlets and switches by means of an approved fitting. BX boxes are provided with devices which permit cables to be run directly into holed openings, where clamps hold the cable in place. However, octagon and square boxes, service switches, in fact, all exposed units, are entered by means of knockouts (disks partially cut). A squeeze connector, shown in the illustration which has a threaded end and a locknut, is used to secure BX cable in place where knockouts are used as the means of entry (Fig. 6.82).

There are times where it is necessary to run BX at right angles to a knock-out, thus restricting the room available for a free bend. This is true at the service. An angle BX connector will permit parallel entry to a knockout.

Outlet Boxes. Bar-supported outlet boxes are useful for new installations because the bar hanger does away with the necessity of bridging to provide fastening for the box. Nails may be used to secure the bar to the underside

FIG. 6.82. BX connectors, squeeze and angle. *Courtesy of Appleton Electric Co.*

of beams, although wood screws are preferable (holes are provided in the bar for this purpose at either end). The outlet box may be adjusted a limited distance either way along the bar by releasing the ⅜″ locknut on the stud inside of the box, moving the box to the desired position and finally retightening the locknut securely.

FIG. 6.83. Outlet boxes, flat bar and deep offset. *Courtesy of Appleton Electric Co.*

Bar-supported outlet boxes may be obtained in several depths, as shown in Fig. 6.83. Flat bar types require a canopy-type fixture because of the shallowness of the box. Deep offset bar types provide plenty of concealment for splices and wiring. Set screws threaded into each cable point of entry provide the means of securing BX cables to the outlet.

Ceiling boxes without bar hangers are suitable for finished house work, since they may be secured directly to the underside of beams, thus providing secure anchorage without damaging the ceiling proper. Wood screws are used for fastening. Cables enter through knockouts provided in the back of the box, and are held in place by clamps, which are tightened by means of set screws.   See Fig. 6.84 A and B.

BX cable boxes may be used for general purposes for nearly every type of outlet, except ceiling and floor outlets.   They are used for wall brackets, switch outlets, receptacle outlets, and in many other places around the home.   Boxes of this type are made for concealed installations, and are

Fig. 6.84A.   Ceiling BX box, usually fastened to under side of beam.

Fig. 6.84B.   BX boxes for wall mounting.

Fig. 6.84C.   Staple for BX cable.

Courtesy of Appleton Electric Co.

intended to finish flush with plaster or woodwork.   For mounting on the faces of studs, these boxes are made with extended ears.   Wood screws through the ears hold the box rigidly in place without any other support.

Lip supports (which do not protrude beyond the width of the box) are useful in securing the boxes to lath for finished house wiring.   Patented clamps, screw operated, are used to secure BX cables to the boxes.   No BX connector is needed with this type of box, since the clamps serve the same purpose.

BX Cable Staples.   A convenient means of fastening BX cables for both exposed and concealed work on wood surfaces is by means of staples.   These staples are large enough to fit over a cable and have a fairly rigid striking surface.   However, when driving staples over cables care should be exercised not to drive the staple in too far, causing injury to armor and wires.

Ackerman-Johnson expansive screw anchors are designed for attaching any object to hard materials, such as concrete, brick, stone, tile, marble, etc. These anchors consist essentially of a sleeve which is to be installed in the concrete or brick structure, and which contains a conical inner part.   This arrangement is such that the greater the load attached, the greater is the force wedging the cone against the sleeve.   In fact, the holding power of this attachment is actually greater than the tensile strength of any ordinary screw or bolt (Fig. 6.85).

Ackerman-Johnson's, as they are called, may be obtained to fit standard sized screws as: $\frac{6}{32}$, $\frac{8}{32}$, $\frac{10}{24}$, $\frac{12}{24}$, etc. A star drill is used to drill to proper depth the hole required by the anchor.

Installing a Base Receptacle Outlet in a Finished Bedroom. The installation of a base receptacle in a room is an excellent project in BX wiring. It has the immediate practical value of filling a need, so frequently expressed by housewives, for additional base receptacles or plugs. Loose wires are a fire hazard that is in violation of every electrical code and are, moreover, extremely unsightly in appearance.

FIG. 6.85. Ackerman-Johnson expansive screw anchor and setting punch.

A further purpose served by this project is that it develops two of the most important skills required in practical electrical work. They consist of the actual installation and connection of the BX wiring and, first of all, of the analysis of the existing circuit to determine how the new wiring should be connected to it. This process is called "circuit analysis" by the electrician. Obviously, it is not necessary where a wiring diagram of the existing installation can be obtained. But this is very seldom the case when the wiring in a finished house is to be remodeled or supplemented. Therefore, the electrician must be able to determine how the house is wired, especially that circuit upon which work is to be done.

This specific problem, as it arises in this project, is to find out how the connections have been made in a room which contains a ceiling electrical fixture controlled by a wall switch. The first step is to turn on the light in the room, then to go to the fuse box (often located in the basement), and remove the fuse or fuses which control the current feeding that fixture. Positive evidence that the right fuse or fuses have been removed is given when the light goes out. This first step is imperative, both for the protection of the system and the workman.

After the circuit has been disconnected, obtain a stepladder, and "drop" the bedroom fixture. Dropping a fixture means releasing it from its fastenings so that it hangs only by the wiring. This may be done without damage if the fixture is lowered gently until the wires take up the strain of its weight. Of course, before the fixture is dropped, the lamp or lamps should be removed.

Now examine the wiring in the ceiling fixture to determine how the connections have been made, and therefore, what circuit has been used to connect switch, lamp, and supply. In the great majority of installations, it will be found that one of three circuits has been used and, therefore, this explanation will be limited to these three. In the first circuit, the feed and ground wires from the two-wire house system are run to the switch first, and from the switch to the ceiling light. If this circuit has been used, the new outlet cannot be tapped from the wires at the ceiling fixture, because the new outlet

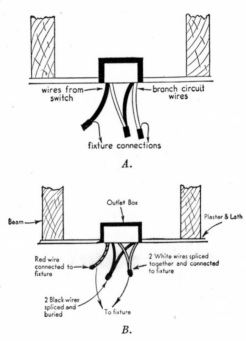

Fig. 6.86.   Connection at fixture outlet for switch control.

would only have current when the bedroom switch and the bedroom light were turned on. In that case, it is necessary to run the new wiring all the way from the bedroom switch. However, the other two commonly used circuits do permit the connection of the new outlet at the ceiling fixture, and this project will, therefore, be planned for that type of installation.

The circuit from the wires and connections found above the ceiling fixture must be understood. In the first circuit, it was stated that two wires are run from the switch to the fixture. Therefore, if this circuit has been used, there will be only two wires at the fixture, one black and one white. (By standard code practice, white wire, or wire with a white tracer, must be used for ground or neutral wires, and black wire must be used for feed or live wires.) If there are only two wires, the fixture should be replaced and the new installation run from the bedroom switch. Since, however, this first method of connection is not the most common, this project will be planned to connect the new outlet at the ceiling leads, as is possible where the existing installation is found to be wired by either the second or the third method.

The connections at the ceiling fixture for these two methods are shown in Fig. 6.86. In this illustration, the existing leads are denoted by heavy lines, and the connections to the present fixture are indicated by light lines. From Fig. 6.86A, it will be seen that, in the second possible circuit, two black wires and two white wires are present at the ceiling outlet. The circuit that has this particular group of connections at the fixture is one in which two 2-wire cables terminate in the outlet, one from the switch, and one from the supply. In grounded interior systems, this end-cable between fixture and switch is called a "switch-loop" and is connected at the fixture as shown in Fig. 6.86A. When connections for the new receptacle are made at the fixture, care must be exercised to tap on to the white and black wires coming from the source of supply and not those going to the switch.

From Fig. 6.86B, it will be seen that, in the third possible circuit for connecting a ceiling fixture, switch, and supply, two black wires, two white wires, and a red (or other color) wire are present at the ceiling outlet. The two black wires will have been spliced, taped, and buried, the two white wires will have been spliced and connected in the fixture, and the red wire will have been connected to the other side of the fixture. The circuit that has this particular group of connections at the fixture is one in which one three-wire cable and one two-wire cable run to the fixture — the three-wire cable from the switch and the two-wire cable from the supply or from another outlet. The wires for the new outlet are tapped as shown in Fig. 6.86B, one from the white wires and one from the black wires, conveniently at the junctions. The connections of the ceiling fixture are shown diagrammatically in Fig. 6.87.

In both the circuits described above, it will be noted that a point on a black wire and a point on a white wire have been chosen for the tap for the new outlet. From these two points, a circuit for the new installation is planned as shown in Fig. 6.88. By studying this circuit, it is clear that only a single BX 2-wire cable (No. 14 wire) is needed from the bedroom ceiling outlet to the new base receptacle. From this point on the project becomes more a matter of mechanical skill than electrical knowledge. Therefore, the physical conditions to be encountered in installing the cable will be discussed.

If the attic in the house is accessible, the problem is somewhat simplified, for it can be used for running the cable from the bedroom ceiling outlet

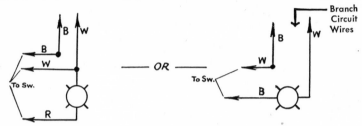

FIG. 6.87.   Diagrammatic connection of ceiling fixtures.

B — Black wire (+); W — White wire (−); R — Red wire (switch leg).

(which is visible in an unfloored attic, and easily reached by removing a small portion of flooring in a floored attic).   Figure 6.90 and 6.75 (page 65) show the proposed run of cable from ceiling outlet to the partition through which the cable will run to the new receptacle.   A closet wall has been selected

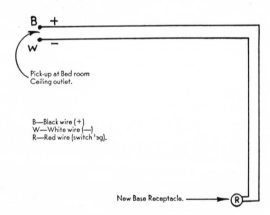

FIG. 6.88.   Wiring plan for new installation.

for the location of the receptacle, because it is necessary to make a hole in the plaster wall to by-pass the bridging which reinforces the studding, and because the plaster patch is much less noticeable on the inside wall of the closet.

To start the actual installation, cut an opening in the baseboard to recess a BX box which will house the new receptacle.

Mark the outline of the box against the baseboard, holding the box so that the longest sides are parallel to the floor, as shown in Fig. 6.90. Use a standard BX box with lips for fastening.

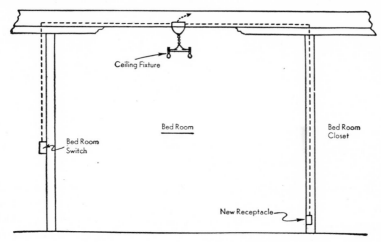

FIG. 6.89. Plan of installation — sectional view.

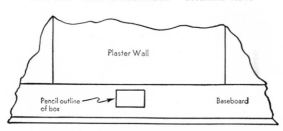

FIG. 6.90. Laying out for the receptacle box.

Using a ½″ wood bit and a brace, bore four holes, one in each corner within the outline of the box, as shown in Fig. 6.91. Next, use a compass or keyhole saw to cut out the wood along the lines between the holes. The box must recess without hindrance. Place the BX box in the hole and lay out for the fastening lips by marking around their edges with a pencil. These lips, one on each side of the box, are to be recessed only until they fit flush, or about ⅛″. A sharp wood chisel is used for this purpose.

More preparation has to be done before the cable can be run. Inside of the closet, directly over the receptacle hole in the baseboard and about 5′ off the floor, sound the wall with the handle of a screwdriver, or hammer lightly and try to locate the bridging between studs by the sound. The position of the bridging is indicated by a "solid" sound, as contrasted with the hollow sound obtained elsewhere.

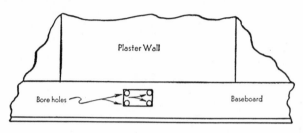

FIG. 6.91.   Boring holes.

A vertical cut should then be made by tapping a small chisel or screwdriver lightly with the flat of a hammer head, continuing the process until the lath is revealed. The purpose of this cut is to permit the cable to pass the bridging. This cut should extend about 2″ above and 2″ below the bridging (see Fig. 6.92). Then it is extended through the lath by a keyhole saw or a compass saw.

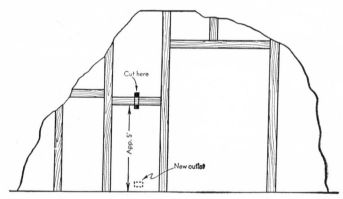

FIG. 6.92.   Sketch showing approximate location of bridging and cut to be made inside closet to permit passage of BX cable.

The next operation is done from the attic and consists of boring a hole through the partition block, directly over the point where the cable will be dropped to meet the cut made on the inside closet wall. The position of this partition is visible in an unfloored attic and can be found in a floored attic by removing a board. The hole through the partition block is bored with a

$\frac{5}{8}''$ wood bit, which makes a hole which a BX two-wire No. 14 cable can pass through freely.

The cable can now be installed. The run should start from the attic. Skin about 1' of armor and run from the ceiling outlet along the bay to the hole leading down through the closet partition. Push 5 or more feet of cable through the hole, then see that pressure from below will move the cable freely. Next, go to the bedroom closet and fish out the end of the BX. A piece of stiff wire with a short hook on the end will serve as a snake for this purpose. Pull out enough cable to reach the receptacle outlet below, then feed it down through the partition past the bridging. Go then to the recep-

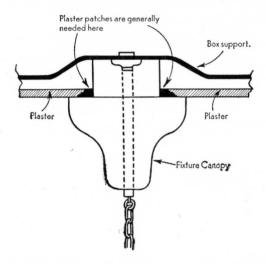

FIG. 6.93. Closing air gaps between plaster and outlet box.

tacle outlet at the baseboard in the bedroom and fish out the cable end as before, using a short snake wire. Place an "anti-short" under the armor of the BX, remove a knockout from the BX box, and secure the cable to the box. A clamp and set screw inside the box serve this purpose. The BX box is then fitted in place and held to the baseboard permanently by means of four No. 4, $\frac{1}{4}''$, flat head wood screws fastened through the lips.

Next, go to the closet and draw up the slack cable, forcing it upward into the hollow above the bridging. Drive a BX staple into the bridging over the cable to prevent the cable from breaking through the plaster patch. Draw the slack cable into the attic. (See Fig. 6.89 again.) Square off the cable where it runs over beams and fasten it well below the top with staples or straps where it runs parallel to the sides of the beams.

At the ceiling outlet allow 1′ for splicing beyond the box and cut the cable. Skin back about 8″, using a hack saw to cut the armor. Open a knockout and push the skinned cable through, after having placed an "anti-short" under the armor. Strap the cable securely in place in the attic and provide wood protectors the same height as the cable where the cable crosses the beams.

Mix some plaster of Paris and seal the hole in the closet where the cable passed the bridging. Next, connect the receptacle unit to the wire ends at the receptacle and fasten the receptacle to the box with $6/32$ machine screws. Put on the receptacle cover. The last operation is to connect the new cable at the fixture into the circuit by splicing, as shown in Fig. 6.86. All splices should be soldered and well taped. Put the fixture back in place. See Fig. 6.93 for a method of closing air gaps around the fixture.

The project is now completed except for testing. The "lamp in cutout" method described elsewhere (Conduit Chapter) is recommended to ensure a safe installation.

Chapter 6

ELECTRICAL WIRING IN RIGID CONDUIT

Code Requirements . . . Bending Conduit . . . Conduit and Fittings: Conduit, Straps, Locknuts, and Bushings, Outlet Boxes, Threaded Unilets, Unilet Covers and Fittings, No-Thread Unilets, Threaded Unilet Switch Bodies, Unilet Outlet Boxes . . . Installing a Switch-Controlled Light in a Garage . . . Installing a Reflector Light Over a Garage Door

Rigid conduit is the name of a type of pipe used by electricians to contain electrical conductors. Its installation in home wiring offers certain definite advantages over other methods of electrical installation. For permanency, for maximum protection against mechanical and electrical injury to the wiring, and for ease of replacement of wires in the event of electrical troubles or changes, conduit wiring is the best. In fact, its use is often required by various codes for wiring in specified locations. The New York City Code now requires that "exposed" circuits be run in conduit, except under restrictions, which usually apply to only a small part of the wiring.

Code Requirements. In planning a conduit installation, one of the first questions to be considered is the number of wires to be run in the conduit, which depends, in turn, partly upon the current to be carried. Both of these factors, that is, the amount of current which may be carried by a wire of given size, and the number of wires of any given size which may be installed in conduit, are specified in many of the codes. If the local code or local regulations do not contain such specifications, the home mechanic is advised to follow the National Electrical Code. Table 1 is a portion of Table 1, from Chapter 10 of this Code, which gives the allowable current-carrying capacities, in amperes, for wires of various sizes. It will be noted that No. 14 wire is the smallest size listed, because it is the smallest that should ever be installed in a lighting or power circuit. Table 2, which is a portion of Table 4, Chapter 10 of the National Electrical Code, shows the number of conductors of any given size which may be installed in the various sizes of conduit. Thus, by use of Table 1 and Table 2, it is possible to determine the number of wires necessary to carry any required current, and the size of the conduit in which they should be installed. This decides, in the absence

TABLE 1. ALLOWABLE CURRENT-CARRYING CAPACITIES OF CONDUCTORS IN AMPERES
Not More Than Three Conductors in Raceway or Cable
(Based on Room Temperature of 30 C. 86 F.)

Size AWG MCM	Rubber Type R Type RW Type RU (14–6) / Thermoplastic Type T Type TW (14–4/0)	Rubber Type RH	Paper Thermoplastic Asbestos Type TA / Var-Cam Type V / Asbestos Var-Cam Type AVB	Asbestos Var-Cam Type AVA Type AVL	Impregnated Asbestos Type AI (14–8) Type AIA	Asbestos Type A (14–8) Type AA
14	15	15	25	30	30	30
12	20	20	30	35	40	40
10	30	30	40	45	50	55
8	40	45	50	60	65	70
6	55	65	70	80	85	95

TABLE 2. NUMBER OF CONDUCTORS IN CONDUIT OR TUBING
Rubber Covered, Types RF-32, R, RH, RW and RU Thermoplastic, Types TF, T and TW
One to Nine Conductors
For more than nine conductors see Table 9.
(See sections 3013, 3466, and 3486)

Size AWG MCM	Number of Conductors in One Conduit or Tubing								
	1	2	3	4	5	6	7	8	9
18	½	½	½	½	½	½	½	¾	¾
16	½	½	½	½	½	½	¾	¾	¾
14	½	½	½	½	¾	¾	1	1	1
12	½	½	½	¾	¾	1	1	1	1¼
10	½	¾	¾	¾	1	1	1	1¼	1¼
8	½	¾	¾	1	1¼	1¼	1¼	1½	1½
6	½	1	1	1¼	1½	1½	2	2	2
4	½	1¼	1¼	1½	1½	2	2	2	2½
3	¾	1¼	1¼	1½	2	2	2	2½	2½
2	¾	1¼	1¼	2	2	2	2½	2½	2½
1	¾	1½	1½	2	2½	2½	2½	3	3

of any other specific local code directives, the size of conduit to be chosen for a specific job.

There are a few other requirements regarding the use of conduit that are so general in the various codes that they should be followed in all conduit work, even in localities where they are not mandatory. No conduit smaller than

½", electrical trade size, should ever be used.   Before installation of wires, all ends of lengths of conduit should be reamed to remove rough edges, which might damage the insulation on wires as they are being drawn through a conduit.   When a conduit enters a box or other fitting, a bushing must be provided to protect the wire from abrasion, unless the design of the box or fitting is such as to supply equivalent protection.   Rigid metal conduit may be used under all conditions and occupancies, except that conduit and fittings protected from corrosion solely by enamel may be used only indoors, because

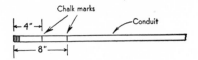

Fig. 6.94.   Measuring for the bend.

this finish is not watertight.   Conduit for outside purposes is usually galvanized to make it watertight.   Of course, conduit and fittings exposed to severe corrosive conditions must be of corrosion-resistant material suitable to the conditions.

Bending Conduit.   Conduit is made chiefly of iron, but differs in this respect from ordinary pipe in that considerable tin and metal scrap is used in its manufacture, so that it is readily bent to make special shapes required on the job.   To meet code requirements, bends must be made without injuring

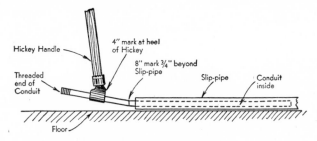

Fig. 6.95.   Starting the bend.

the conduit and without effectively reducing its internal diameter.   Furthermore, the radius of the circle of curvature of the inside of any bend must not be less than six times the diameter of the conduit.   The tool commonly used for bending conduit is the hickey, which is used as described in the following account of the bending of a 90° elbow.

In making this elbow any convenient piece of conduit may be used, or a standard length may be taken. (Conduit comes in standard, 10′ lengths, threaded on both ends, and provided at one end of each length with a coupling, which is used for joining sections of conduit together to form a continuous run.) Assume that an 8″ elbow is to be made on a piece of ½″ conduit. Lay the length, or piece of conduit, on the floor and mark upon it, with white chalk, two rings — one 4″ from the end, and the other 8″ from the end, as shown in Fig. 6.94. It will be noted that the distance of this second mark, 8″ from the end, is the full length of the elbow to be bent. Now place a slip pipe (1″ plumber's pipe about 4′ long) over the conduit to within ¾″ of the 8″ chalk mark, as shown in Fig. 6.95. Next, place the hickey over the conduit, with the bending part at rest on the 4″ chalk mark.

Place one foot against the hickey, between the hickey head and the slip pipe, to prevent slippage. Now start the bending by pulling the hickey handle forward, a little at a time. After each small bend, or "bite," the hickey should be moved slightly along the conduit toward the slip pipe. This will ensure a rounded head. From time to time during the bending, the shape of the bend should be checked with a rule, to make sure that the bend is not becoming too long or too short.

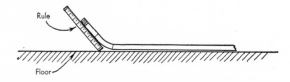

FIG. 6.96. Checking the partially completed bend.

Figure 6.96 illustrates how this checking should be done. First, remove the slip pipe, so that the conduit rests firmly on the floor. Hold the partially completed bend in a vertical rule butting the floor. (See Fig. 6.96.) At

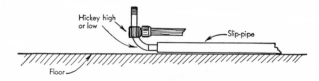

FIG. 6.97. Completing the elbow.

this point the bend may be too high or too low to produce a finished 8″ bend. This variation is compensated, either way, by placing the hickey accordingly in its final bending position, shown in Fig. 6.97. Thus, if the elbow is too low, placing the hickey low on the bend near the slip pipe will raise it; whereas, if the elbow is becoming too high, placing the hickey high on the bend will reduce the final height of the elbow.

A final check is made of the height of the elbow. To make this measurement, remove the slip pipe and place a rule butting the floor and parallel to the bend end as shown in Fig. 6.98.

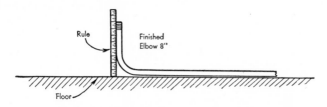

FIG. 6.98. Checking length of vertical section.

Conduit and Fittings. *Conduit.* Electrical conduit (see Fig. 6.99) may be obtained in different sizes, from the smallest permitted by the code, $\frac{1}{2}''$, up to immense sizes for industrial use, $4''$ and $6''$. Standard conduit sizes are: $\frac{1}{2}''$, $\frac{3}{4}''$, $1''$, $1\frac{1}{4}''$, $1\frac{1}{2}''$, $2''$, $2\frac{1}{2}''$, $3''$, $3\frac{1}{2}''$, $4''$, etc. Conduit is supplied in standard $10'$ lengths, threaded on both ends, and each length is furnished with one coupling which is used to join sections of conduit to form one continuous conduit run.

FIG. 6.99. Electrical conduit.

Changes of direction in conduit installations are accomplished by bending the conduit or by using fittings to take the place of bends. After conduit is installed, the wires are drawn through it by means of a snake. Conduit for inside wiring is enamel finished and, for outdoor work, is galvanized.

Straps. Conduit must be rigidly fastened in place when installed. This fastening is commonly accomplished by means of straps. For exposed conduit work, straps must be placed within a foot of each outlet, and not more than 4' apart, along a conduit run.

Two kinds of straps are available, one-hole straps (see Fig. 6.100) and two-hole straps. One-hole straps are more convenient to use. Two-hole straps provide double fastening. Wood screws make good anchors in wood backing. Where conduit is run across the face of a brick wall, Rawl-plugs or Ackerman-Johnston anchors should be used.

FIG. 6.100.   One-hole strap.

FIG. 6.101.   Locknut.

FIG. 6.102.   Bushing.

FIG. 6.103.   Capped bushing.

Courtesy of Appleton Electric Co.

Locknuts and Bushings. Locknuts are used to keep conduits firmly anchored to outlets and boxes, while bushings serve the same purpose, in addition to providing a smooth surface for wires to enter or leave conduits. Capped bushings are installed temporarily to keep foreign objects from entering a conduit, from the time it is installed until wires are drawn in place (see Figs. 6.101, 6.102, and 6.103).

Locknuts and bushings are sized exactly the same as conduit. Thus, if ½" conduit wire is being used for an installation, ½" locknuts and bushings should also be used.

Outlet Boxes. Conduits must be terminated at fixtures, switches, receptacles, and at similar equipment. For general use the 4" square box, sometimes known as the "1900 box," is recommended. It has the advantage of many knockouts for the entrance of conduits, and it provides ample room for burying wires. The 4" square box may be used for fixture outlets, switches, and receptacles. Various covers, each suited to a particular purpose, may be obtained to fit the box (see Fig. 6.104).

A 4″ round or octagonal box may serve the same purpose as the square box, except that it will not take flush switches.

Round boxes (octagonal in shape) may be obtained in 3″ sizes and are useful where less space is required.

| 4″ sq. box. | 4″ sq. outlet box cover. | 4″ sq. switch cover. | 4″ octagon outlet box. |

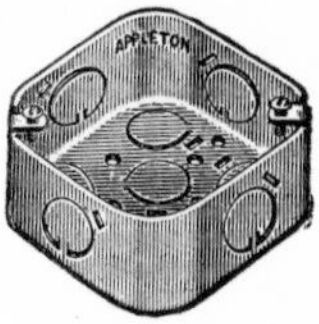

FIG. 6.104. Conduit boxes and covers. *Courtesy of Appleton Electric Co.*

Threaded Unilets. Unilets are patented fittings which may be used in place of conduit bends. Their installation eliminates bending in running conduit, and leaves only cutting and threading as the two major operations in a conduit job. They may be used on exposed work only.

Type E Unilet.   Type C Unilet.

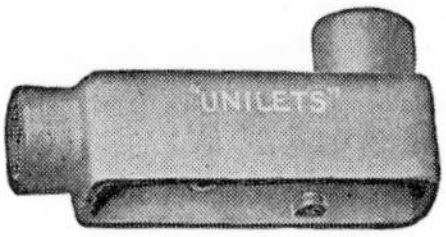

Type LB Unilet.   Type LF Unilet.

FIG. 6.105. Unilets. *Courtesy of Appleton Electric Co.*

Unilets are known by letters (see Fig. 6.105). An E-type Unilet would be used for an end line. A C-type Unilet would be used to provide a splice point in a continuous run of conduit. Unilets may be obtained for every purpose. A good electrical catalog will show a large variety of shapes to meet every need.

No-thread Unilets (see Fig. 6.106) serve the same general purpose as the threaded Unilet, except that no conduit threading is necessary during the installation. Thus, it is possible to do a complete conduit installation with little or no threading. A ferrule is provided under each threaded entrance point of no-thread Unilets which, when the threaded cap is tightened, will force the ferrule into position, thereby securing the conduit firmly in place.

Threaded Unilet Switch Bodies.   Where Unilets are employed in a conduit installation, special fittings should be used at switches and outlets.   An example of a threaded switch body is shown in Fig. 6.107.

Unilet Outlet Boxes.   Just as special fittings are used at switch outlets in an installation using Unilets, so are special outlet boxes provided for light fixtures, as shown in Fig. 6.108.

Unilet Covers and Fittings.   Porcelain lamp receptacles are available for Unilet outlets as shown in Fig. 6.109.   These receptacles are round in shape and fasten directly to the Unilet by means of machine screws.

A Unilet switch cover for Unilet switch boxes is shown in Fig. 6.110.   The cover fastens to the switch unit by means of machine screws and has a bent back edge which joins snugly with the switch box to form a smooth finish.

Figure 6.111 shows a Unilet duplex receptacle cover to fit over the receptacle shown in Fig. 6.113.   Both are made rectangular in shape to meet the requirements of the Unilet and are secured in place by machine screws.

Figure 6.112 shows a Unilet lamp receptacle which may be used with standard Unilet fittings.

Figure 6.114 shows a blank Unilet cover and a gasket to seal off a standard Unilet fitting.

Installing a Switch-Controlled Light in a Garage.   One-car and two-car garages are often entirely lacking in electric service.   The garage may have been neglected in the original building plans because of its distance from the house, or because it was constructed some time after the house was built, or simply because no lighting was installed.   Whatever the reason, the absence of electric lighting from the garage is a serious inconvenience which, the home-mechanic will be glad to learn, is well within his ability to remedy. For while this job might appear at first glance to be an ambitious undertaking, it will be found to require no high degree of skill.   Common sense plus ordinary dexterity are sufficient, if every direction given in this project is carried out methodically.

All these directions have, of course, been prepared in accordance with code requirements.   The code followed here is the National Electrical Code, which is representative in that its standards are those of safety and good practice, and it meets the requirements of most local authorities.   However, some local codes, including that of New York City, are now more rigid in some of their provisions than the National Electrical Code.   Therefore, the home mechanic is urged to consult his local authorities about their require-

Type C.

Type E.

Type LB.

Type LF.

Fig. 6.106. Types C, E, LB, and LF no-thread Unilets.

Fig. 6.107. Threaded Unilet body, shallow, single-gang.

Fig. 6.108. Unilet outlet box.

Fig. 6.109. Porcelain lamp receptacle.

Fig. 6.110. Unilet switch cover.

Fig. 6.111. Unilet receptacle outlet cover.

Fig. 6.112. Unilet lamp receptacle.

Fig. 6.113. Unilet rectangular duplex receptacle.

Fig. 6.114. Unilet blank cover and gasket.

Courtesy of Appleton Electric Co.

ments. This is especially important for new installations, including this project, because some communities require that a permit be obtained for electrical installations in systems operating above 23 volts. Where such code provisions are in force, you must obtain a temporary permit covering this installation only, by application to the proper local authority before any actual work is begun.

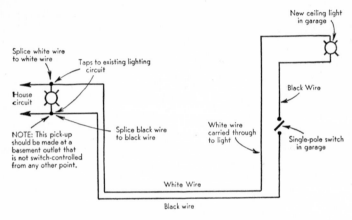

FIG. 6.115. Wiring diagram for garage switch-controlled light.

As in all installations in this book, this job will be planned from a wiring diagram of the circuit. Such a diagram is given in Fig. 6.115 and shows a switch-controlled garage light that is connected to a "feed" (source of supply) at an existing basement outlet, preferably one located near the basement wall at a point closest to the garage. Two considerations govern the selection of this outlet. It should be independently connected, that is, it should not be controlled by a switch from any other point. Furthermore, it should not be chosen in a circuit that is already carrying its full rated current. (See the table of allowable capacities of wires, in the earlier part of this chapter.)

The next step is to prepare from the wiring diagram (Fig. 6.115) a sketch of the actual installation (Fig. 6.116). This sketch should be drawn with sufficient accuracy so that the required measurements can be made on the site of the installation. Examine this sketch closely and note that the wires are to be installed in conduit for the underground run, but that BX is used inside the basement and the garage. This type of installation complies with the National Electrical Code. There are some localities, such as New York

City, in which the local code requires all "exposed" wiring to be run in conduit, except under restrictions. Under such codes, of course, practically this entire job must be done in conduit.

Next proceed to prepare an estimate of materials required in the sketch (Fig. 6.116). It will be noted that where BX cable joins conduit, which happens at one point in the garage and another in the basement, a box is shown in Fig. 6.116. These are called pull boxes, and their installation at these junctions is required by code to contain and protect the junctions between wires that result when BX changes to conduit, or the reverse. For use as pull boxes at these two points, choose a 3" octagon box with ½" knockouts

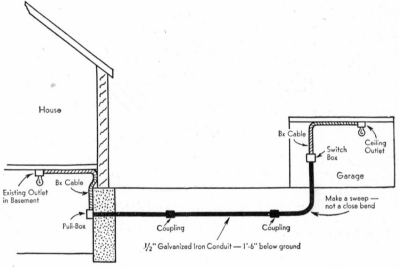

FIG. 6.116. Complete installation.

for installation in the basement and a 4" square box with a switch cover for installation in the garage. The 4" square box will serve in the double capacity of a pull box to connect conduit and BX, and a switch box to hold the switch that controls the garage light. One more 3" octagon box (making two in all) is needed for installation at the light outlet in the garage, this box to have a lamp receptacle cover which holds the lamp receptacle for the light.

The next step is to determine the amount of BX cable, conduit, and wire that is required. As shown in Fig. 6.116, BX is used from the existing outlet in the basement to the pull box where the conduit leaves the basement, and also from the switch box in the garage to the garage light. Choose No. 14,

BX two-wire cable as the size desired (No. 14 BX is the smallest permissible under the Code). Find the length of this cable required in the basement by measuring the distance across the basement ceiling from the existing outlet, then down the side basement wall to the pull box, and add 2' to this total for splicing purposes. In this particular job, the dimensions are found as shown in Fig. 6.117. The distance across the basement ceiling, from existing outlet to a point directly above the pull box, is 6', and the distance down the wall to the pull box is 4', so $6' + 4' + 2' = 12'$ of BX, two-wire, No. 14 cable will be needed for the basement end of the installation.

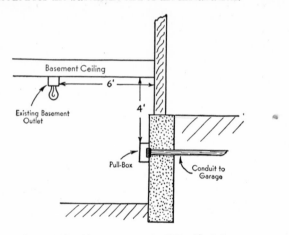

Fig. 6.117. Measurements for BX cable in basement.

In order to figure the length of BX cable needed in the garage, the first step is to establish the location of the 4'' square box, which serves as both pull box and switch box. Its position is determined by the position of the switch it mounts, which should be near the door and 4' from the finished floor of the garage. Next, locate the light, which should be placed in the ceiling midway between the side walls of the garage, but closer to the closed end than to the doors. This is done to favor the front of the car. In this particular job, the garage measures $16' \times 10'$. Therefore, the length of cable required is the distance from center to side wall (5'), plus the distance along the top of the wall back to a point above the switch (about 8'), plus the distance down to the switch (about 4'). Adding these figures, plus 2' for connections, $5' + 8' + 4' + 2' = 19'$ of BX cable required for the garage. The total required for the job is the sum of that for basement and garage, or $12' + 19' = 31'$ of two-wire, No. 14 BX cable.

By referring again to Fig. 6.116, it will be seen that the conduit from house to garage runs underground in a trench dug for the purpose. The amount of conduit will be determined by deciding upon the layout of the trench and by measuring the run. In this particular job, the distance of the garage from the house is 20'. To this must be added 1' through the basement wall, plus 6' up to the switch at the garage end, making a total of 27' of conduit. Since, however, conduit is supplied in 10' lengths, enter 30' on the material estimate. Since it is to be used outdoors, specify galvanized conduit, and since it contains only two No. 14 wires, ½" conduit is ample in size. For installation in this underground conduit, we will require 27' + 2' (for splicing) = 29' of lead covered, No. 14, duplex wire.

The equipment and wiring so far specified includes two 3" octagon boxes, one with blank cover and one with lamp receptacle cover, one 4" square switch box with switch cover, single-pole switch and plate, as well as the necessary cable, conduit, and wiring. Fittings will also be needed for various purposes. The BX cable requires terminating fittings that are called connectors. Four of them are required: one to enter the existing outlet in the basement, one for the cable connection to the basement pull box, one for the cable to the switch box in the garage, and a fourth to connect the cable to the garage ceiling light. Anti-short protectors are also needed for each cable end, four in all. Incidental materials that are essential to do this job are a number of BX staples to support the BX cable, No. 8 1" wood screws to attach the boxes, a small supply of red lead to make the conduit joints, as well as solder and tape. The complete list is as follows:

BILL OF MATERIALS

Item	Amount
No. 14 BX cable, two-wire	31'
½" galvanized iron conduit	30'
BX connectors	4
3" octagon boxes	2
3" lamp receptacle	1
3" blank cover	1
4" square box	1
4" square box switch cover	1
Single-pole switch and plate	1
No. 14 Duplex lead-covered wire	29'
BX cable staples	
Wood screws, 1", No. 8	1½ doz.
Red lead	small can
Wire solder paste	
Tape, rubber, and friction	

Installation. The best way to install this job is to complete all the work from the basement pull box to the light and switch in the garage before making the pick-up to the existing basement outlet. That particular operation is left until the last, although of course, it was chosen before the job was planned.

Before commencing the installation, make provision for running the ½″ conduit out of the basement. This is easily arranged if there is a basement window frame suitable for boring with a 13⁄16″ wood bit. In that case,

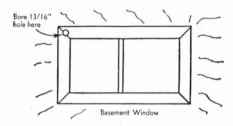

Fɪɢ. 6.118. Locating hole to reach basement.

simply make a hole in the corner of the window frame as shown in Fig. 6.118. Then, if this would bring our external conduit run too high, modify the conduit run accordingly by the use of another bend in the outside conduit, at the house end. If there is no basement window which can be closed permanently for this installation, the wall must be drilled.

Cutting Through Concrete or Cement Block Foundations. Concrete and cement block foundations are not difficult to drill. Best results are obtained if the hole is started from the basement side, because the first break-through often releases a large piece of the surface of the material, and this is not desirable on the inside where a patch would show. The hole should be made at a point at least 18″ below the ground line, or more in very cold places. A 1″ star drill is the best tool for drilling concrete, using a mason's hammer, or a heavy machinist's hammer for striking it. If no star drill is available, a handy substitute can be made from a piece of ¾″ plumber's pipe, about 14″ to 16″ in length. One end of the pipe (threadless) should be notched as shown in Fig. 6.5; a hack saw may be used for the purpose, while the pipe is held securely in a vise.

After establishing a means for running the conduit out of the basement, the next step is to dig a trench, of shovel-width, from the point of exit (or entry) into the basement to a point below the location of our switch in the garage. This trench should be deep enough to bring the conduit at least

18″ below the ground surface, or even deeper in northern latitudes, where the frost line is deeper. The position of the hole in the basement wall is chosen, of course, low enough to give the conduit the proper depth below the ground.

If this is not done, it will be necessary to make a bend in the conduit outside the wall to reach the proper depth.

If, however, the hole is placed so it is sufficiently below ground level, the simplest method of installing the conduit is to start from its end at the switch box in the garage. Remove one of the ½″ knockouts from the top of the 4″ square box and remove another knockout from the bottom. The knockouts

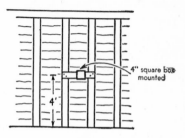

FIG. 6.119.   Mounting switch box in garage.

are loosened by tapping with a hammer, and removed by a twisting motion of the pliers. Then, using the No. 8 wood screws, fasten the 4″ square box to a stud in the side wall of the garage near the entrance, at a height of 4′ from the finished floor to the center of the box (see Fig. 6.119).

Measure the distance from the bottom knockout hole in the switch box to the bottom of the trench and bend a 90° elbow at a point in a 10′ length of ½″ conduit that will fit this position. (Methods of bending conduit at 90° are described earlier in this chapter.) A locknut is screwed as far as it will go onto the end of the bent conduit that is to be connected to the switch box. This connection is made by passing the end of the conduit into the knockout opening in the bottom of the box, as far as the locknut will allow it to go. A ½″ bushing is now screwed onto the end of the conduit, inside the box, thus making the wall of the box fast between locknut and bushing. After the first (bent) length of conduit has been installed in this way, the second length of conduit is joined to it by a coupling. In connecting this joint, apply red lead to the threads, and make it up tight with a pipe wrench. Finally, the run of conduit is completed by cutting and threading the third 10′ length of conduit to the proper length to connect with the 3″ octagon box (pull box), which is so located on the basement wall that the knockout opening in its back corresponds to the hole made in the wall. After this third piece of conduit has been connected, the 3″ octagon box is attached to it by a locknut and bushing, exactly as described for the switch box in the garage. The 3″ octagon box is then fastened to the basement wall by the use of Rawlplugs and wood screws.

With the conduit run in place, the garage "roughing" can now be completed. The position of the ceiling light outlet is marked, and a 3″ octagon box is fastened there, using a beam or backboard for support, after first removing a ½″ knockout from the side of the box.   Then the No. 14 BX two-wire cable is secured to the box by the method described in the previous chapter.   The operations in the method consist of skinning the end of the cable, inserting an anti-short under the armor, placing a connector on the cable, and securing the connector to the outlet box by means of the connector locknut.   The BX cable is then secured by straps to beams or other heavy structural members and is run over to the side wall and down to the switch, where the same terminating method is used.

We are now ready to "fish" our lead-covered wires through the conduit from the garage switch to the basement pull box. A "snake" (see Chapter 2) is run through the conduit from garage to basement, the lead-covered wires are made fast to the hook in the end of the snake, and this temporary connection is well taped.   It is then coated with soap flakes or grease to help ease it through the conduit.   Two people are needed to do the "fishing" operation conveniently.   One person should exert an even pull on the snake in the basement, while another feeds the lead-covered wires into the conduit. Pulling and feeding should be done by means of short, even advances of about 1′ at a time, until the wires are in place.

To install the BX cable in the basement, remove the fuse controlling the basement outlet, because the circuit must be "dead" before work is done upon it.   To make sure the right fuse is removed, turn on the basement light, so as to be certain that the removal of the fuse extinguishes the light. Then a two-wire No. 14 BX cable is run from the existing outlet to the pull box.   It is connected to the pull box by skinning the wire, inserting an anti-short under the corner, placing a connector on the cable, and fastening the connector to the pull box, exactly as described for the garage BX connection. The BX cable is supported by straps, as usual, but its actual connection into the existing circuit is deferred until the very end of the job.   However, to measure the proper length of BX and to leave ends long enough for splicing into the existing circuit, it is necessary to work close to that circuit, and therefore the fuse should be removed.

The lead-covered wires may now be connected to the wires from the BX. Start at the garage end and connect, first of all, a lamp receptacle to the wire ends from the BX at the ceiling light outlet.   Next, connect by a pigtail splice (see Chapter 3) the two white wires at the switch box, one from the BX and the other from the pair of lead-covered wires (after first removing the lead covering as far back as the bushing in the box). This splice is soldered, taped, and buried in the usual way. Then connect a single-pole switch across the two black wires at this point. Fasten the switch to the box cover and mount the plate over the switch. This completes the garage part of the installation.

At the pull box on the basement wall, connect the wires by means of two pigtail splices. One of these joins the white wire from the BX with the white lead-covered wire from the conduit, while the other splice joins black to black. Both splices are soldered, taped, and buried, and a blank cover is placed on the box.

The new installation should be complete with the exception of two splices at the existing outlet to tie in with the house circuit. These splices should be made now (last operation), soldered, taped, and buried, and the outlet returned to its former condition by replacing the cover or fixture.

For testing purposes a lamp is inserted in the garage outlet and the garage switch placed in the OFF position. A lamp of the same wattage is placed in the cutout where the fuse was removed. All other lights on the existing circuit should be turned OFF while this test is being made. Turn on the switch in the garage. If the garage lamp and the lamp in the cutout each light with half-brightness, replace the cutout lamp with a fuse and the circuit is correct. If the garage lamp does not light and the cutout lamp burns with full brightness when this test is made (provided all other lamps on the same circuit are off), there is a short circuit and the fuse cannot be replaced until the trouble is located. Examine in the following order:

1. The existing outlet to which the circuit pick-up was made.
2. The switch in the garage.
3. The light in the garage.
4. The pull-box connection.
5. The wiring itself.

Installing a Reflector Light over a Garage Door. It is very convenient to have a means of lighting the area in front of a garage and the driveway approaching it. This is especially true if the garage doorway is narrow, or if the driveway is bordered closely by shrubbery, rock gardens, or other decorative features. Another advantage of this illumination is that it permits automobile engine repairing to be done in the open air on warm nights, instead of inside a stuffy garage. All these purposes may be accomplished by the installation of a reflector light over the garage door to throw a directed beam of light along the approaches to the garage.

In planning this job, it will be assumed that a lighting circuit has already been installed inside the garage, as described in the project given earlier in this chapter. That installation and, in fact, most of the lighting circuits commonly installed in small garages, consist essentially of a single, overhead light which is controlled by a single-pole switch located on the inside side wall, near the entrance to the garage. In this present job, the new, external lighting circuit will be added to the circuit already installed inside the garage.

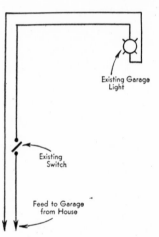

Existing Garage
Light

Existing
Switch

Feed to Garage
from House

FIG. 6.120. Reflector light.   FIG. 6.121. Existing garage   FIG. 6.122. Duplex
                                              circuit.   switch. Single-pole.

As usual, the planning of the job starts from a wiring diagram. Figure 6.121 shows the existing circuit in which, it is to be noted, one of the "feed" (or supply) lines connects directly with the switch. The same switch box can be used for the new circuit without making any major changes at this point, simply by installing a new switch unit which contains two single-pole switches and which fits into the space formerly occupied by the single-pole switch. This unit is called a duplex switch and is shown in Fig. 6.122.

From this new switch and the single "feed" line which was connected to the old switch, the wiring can be planned from this point. Figure 6.123 is a diagram of the new circuit which has been drawn so as to show easily, by direct comparison with Fig. 6.121, just how the new wiring is added and tied in to the existing garage wiring. Figure 6.124 shows how the installation will appear when the job is finished.

The method of installation of the wiring must be governed here, as it should be in every job, by the code requirements. Some codes prohibit the use of BX cable in any exposed position.   Where such a code is in force, the wiring for this entire job, inside as well as outside the garage, must be run in conduit.   The method to be described here will consist of using both conduit

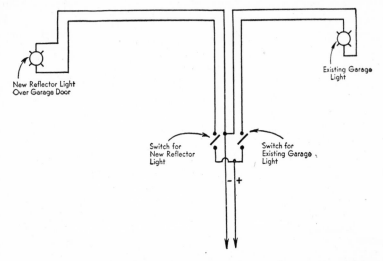

FIG. 6.123.   Existing and new wiring arrangement for installation of reflector light.

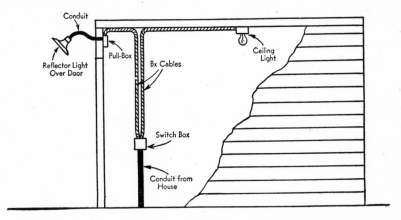

FIG. 6.124.   Appearance of finished installation.

and BX cable.   This method has been chosen because it gives experience in the use of the two methods in combination, and because it is of course permitted by a good many of the codes and local regulations.

The first step in starting work on this job, or for that matter on any other installation, is to remove the fuse which controls the existing circuit. This is safely done by turning on the light in the garage by its switch and by removing the fuse, in the basement cutout, which extinguishes the light in the garage. This is the only *safe* way to work, and it should be a basic procedure of the home mechanic in doing all electrical jobs.

The next step is to locate the position of the reflector light by a pencil mark. A preferred location is on the vertical center line of the garage, midway between the sides and about 6″ down from the top. After this spot is marked on the outside of the building, it should be checked on the inside to make sure there are no 2 × 4's or other obstacles in the way; and if there are, it should be shifted accordingly. Then, using a $1\frac{3}{16}$″ wood bit in a brace, bore a hole from outside to inside at the pencil mark. The $1\frac{3}{16}$″ bit is used because the hole it makes provides a snug fit for $\frac{1}{2}$″ conduit, which is the size to use on this job.

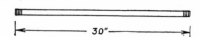

FIG. 6.125.   Conduit ready for bending.

FIG. 6.126.   Gooseneck bend.

Cut a 30″ length of $\frac{1}{2}$″ galvanized conduit, using a hack saw to do the cutting and a vise to hold the conduit. Then ream the inside surface of the conduit at the cut end. The reaming can be done with a standard pipe reamer which is held in a brace or, if there is no reamer available, the reaming may be done with pliers. The method is to rotate the nose of a pair of electrician's pliers in the end of the conduit. Whether pliers or pipe reamer is used, the reaming should be continued until all burrs have been removed from the inside surface of the edge of the conduit, which should feel smooth to the finger.

The next step is to cut outside threads on both ends of the conduit, using a stock and die to do the threading. Three threads past the face of the die are sufficient for conduit.

The 30″ length of conduit, threaded on both ends, is now ready for bending (Fig. 6.125) to form the "gooseneck" which will be used to hold the reflector light. Figure 6.126 shows the gooseneck as it should appear when finished. Before starting the bending, it is best to make a template, or guide pattern, on a flat, rigid surface (bench or floor), using white chalk to draw the outlines. The gooseneck template may be shaped freehand and the conduit bent to this shape.

The bending can be done most conveniently by using an electrician's hickey (see Chapter 2), and a slip pipe (piece of larger sized pipe). Figure 6.127 shows the position of these tools for the first bending operation. The hickey is placed over the conduit near one end, and the slip pipe (a piece of 1″ plumber's pipe will do) is placed over the other end of the conduit to apply pressure and to make the initial bend. Gradual movement of the hickey along the conduit, followed by small applications of pressure by the slip pipe, continue the bending. Several times during this bending procedure the shape of the conduit should be checked against the template to

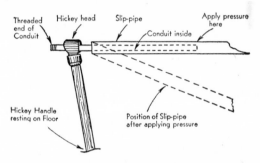

FIG. 6.127. Bending conduit with hickey and slip pipe.

assure that the gooseneck is taking the proper shape. This shape requires that the direction of bending be reversed when the first of the two bends that constitute the gooseneck has been made.

The method just outlined for bending with the hickey, which is explained in greater detail earlier in this chapter, is an important part of the technique of the electrician, or of the home owner who wishes to install conduit. If no hickey is available, a usable substitute is a 1″ tee, which has been made up with a 4′ length of 1″ pipe to serve as a handle.

The gooseneck is put into place by pushing its straight end through the hole over the garage door. A ½″ locknut is then placed on the inside end of the gooseneck, from inside the garage. The locknut is screwed on as far as it will go, and a 3″ pull box is now installed, as shown in Fig. 6.128.

One of the functions of a pull box in electrical work is to contain and protect the junctions between wires which result when a wiring installation changes from conduit to BX cable, and vice versa. In this particular job, since the gooseneck is a conduit, and since BX cable is to be run inside the garage, it will be necessary to install a pull box mechanically connected to the gooseneck. For use as a pull box, choose a 3″ octagon box with ½″ knockouts (Fig. 6.129).

Hold the octagon box on end and remove the back and top knockouts. They should be loosened by tapping them with a hammer, and removed by a twisting motion of the pliers. Now secure the box to the gooseneck by passing the end of the gooseneck into the knockout opening in the back of the box, as far as the locknut on the gooseneck will permit it to go. A ½″ bushing is now screwed onto the end of the gooseneck, inside the box, thus making the wall of the box fast between locknut and bushing (Fig. 6.128). Finally, the box is fastened in place with wood screws.

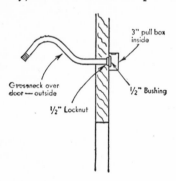
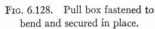

Fig. 6.128. Pull box fastened to bend and secured in place.

Fig. 6.129. 3″ octagon box to be used as pull box.

A length of two-wire BX cable is then secured to the pull box through the knockout hole in the top, by means of a BX connector (see preceding chapter), and the cable is fastened to the under surface of the garage ceiling with cable straps. The cable is run from this point directly to the switch box in the garage. The methods of installation are exactly the same as those given in the preceding chapter on BX cable.

Two pieces of No. 14 lighting wire, lead-covered, one black and the other white, may now be pushed through from the pull box to the end of the gooseneck. Allow enough wire so that about 8″ of each wire will appear beyond the outside of the gooseneck. The reflector light is then secured to the gooseneck, and the light socket is connected to the two leads.

Now return to the pull box and connect the other ends of these leads to the two leads from the BX cable. These connections should be made by pigtail splices (Chapter 3), taking care to connect the white lead from the gooseneck with the white lead from the BX, and the black gooseneck lead with the black BX lead. After soldering and taping the splices, put the blank cover on the box.

The job may now be completed at the switch box. The old switch is removed, and the new duplex switch is connected as shown in the wiring diagram, Fig. 6.123. When all connections have been completed (soldered, taped, and buried), the new switch is secured to the switch box by two $\frac{6}{32}$" screws, and the cover is placed over the switch.

Every new circuit should be tested before leaving the job. There is an excellent method of testing which has the advantage that no damage can result from its use. Obtain a lamp of the same wattage as the reflector lamp which has been installed. Make sure that both switches in the garage are in the OFF position. Now put the lamp in the cutout where the circuit fuse was removed at the start of this job. Make sure all lights in the basement on the garage circuit are turned off for this test. Turn on the switch for the reflector light. If it burns half-bright, the circuit is correct. Now turn off the reflector light switch and proceed to test the garage light circuit in the same way that the reflector light circuit was tested, that is, by making sure both switches are OFF, by installing a lamp in the cutout of the same wattage as the garage light, and by turning on the garage light. It, also, of course, should be half bright. If the lamp in the cutout burns at full brightness, a short circuit is indicated. In such a case, all connections should be examined, beginning at the switch. When the circuits are found to be correct, the testing lamp should be replaced by a fuse.

Chapter 7

ELECTRICAL APPLIANCES

Motorized Appliances. Any electrical appliance which depends upon an electric motor for its operation may be considered as being a motorized appliance. In this group are included the vacuum cleaner, the washing machine, and the electric mixer, among many others. Motorized appliances contain moving parts which constitute a possible source of trouble at all times.

Appliance motors may be designed for use with direct current only, with alternating current only, and with both. The special type of motor which operates on both A.C. and D.C. is known as a "universal" motor.

All appliance motors consist essentially of two elements, one fixed and the other moving. In direct current and universal appliance motors the fixed part contains the magnetic fields, and the moving part is called the armature. In alternating current motors the fixed part is known as the stator, and the moving part is called the rotor.

Two kinds of trouble may develop with any type of appliance motor, electrical trouble or mechanical trouble. Electrical trouble will probably occur more frequently than mechanical trouble.

Electrical Trouble. Several different kinds of electrical trouble may occur, the most frequent of which is an open circuit. An open circuit means that no current will flow through the appliance because the circuit is incomplete or wires are broken. The appliance attachment plug and the appliance cord should be checked first before any tests are made on the appliance motor proper. Following a check of plug and cord the next point to examine is the switch, or controlling device, which starts and stops the appliance motor.

Brush-type motors have brush holders which keep the brushes in place, making contact with the moving armature. These brushes are made of carbon and are held against the commutator surface of the armature by means of springs which exert pressure against the carbon brush. An open circuit may develop when a carbon brush wears down far enough so that its pressure spring no longer is effective, permitting the brush to ride free of the commutator. In this case a new brush should be installed. Sometimes a pressure spring will not function properly as a brush wears down, thus preventing the brush from being forced against the commutator. In this case, removing the spring and stretching it a bit will restore its tension, and it may again be telescoped in the brush holder.

Centrifugal force may be the cause of an open circuit. Wires used for internal motor connections are buried very carefully when the motor is manufactured to prevent their working free, and thus coming into contact with a moving part which would result in injury or damage to the wire. Vibration, caused by rotation of the armature may loosen or gradually move an internal wire out of place into a position where it may become broken. An examination may be made by disassembling the motor and removing the armature. (Brushes must be removed first.)

An open circuit may occur in the armature proper. This may result from several conditions. Overheating may release the commutator leads from their soldered beds. The armature in rotating may strike against some object and sever one or more of its windings. Armature rewinding is a skilled operation, and the home mechanic without previous experience is not advised to try it.

A short circuit is another potential source of trouble with motorized appliances, as well as with all types of electrical appliances. A short circuit occurs when two wires of opposite polarity from the same source of supply come in contact through a very low resistance. It can be readily detected by its effect. The moment a short-circuited motorized appliance is set in motion, usually by switch control, a fuse will blow. Frequently, in addition, a noise accompanied by a flash or spark will indicate the general location of the short circuit in the appliance. Under no circumstance should a short-circuited appliance be attached to the house circuit until the short circuit has been located and cleared.

Sparking at the Brushes. Motorized appliances will frequently spark excessively at the brushes, which is an indication that trouble is developing, if not well under way. Sparking at the brushes may be caused by a poor brush contact due to the brush itself being roughened, worn on one edge, or chipped. A sparking brush should be removed and resurfaced (use sandpaper) to fit the curvature of the commutator with which it is to make contact. Armature trouble, including open and short circuits, will also cause excessive sparking at the brushes.   A third cause is a worn or dirty armature commutator.   Constant use may "groove" it, that is, a deep uneven groove may be worn in the commutator which will prevent a full-faced brush contact.   Also, the commutator may be blackened, dirty, or oil-covered.   A little cleaning with fine sandpaper will restore the commutator to its former clean surface.   The mica insulation between bars on a

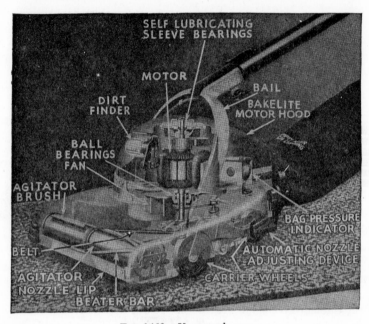

FIG. 6.130.   Vacuum cleaner.

commutator may be high, causing the brush to miss contact with the commutator and thus produce sparking.   A commutator may be resurfaced by turning and cutting in a lathe.

Mechanical Trouble.   Mechanical trouble in an appliance motor will probably manifest itself in the action of the rotating portion of the motor.

Since an armature rotates on a shaft, which is supported between two bearings, more mechanical trouble will occur at the bearings.   Motors should be lubricated with oil or grease regularly.   Failure to lubricate them properly will result in worn bearings or shaft.   A worn bearing or shaft may be detected easily, since it will be noisy.   Bearings in small appliance motors are replaceable.

Electric Clocks. The accuracy of electric clocks depends upon the frequency of the current supplied by the electric company. The clock itself cannot be regulated.

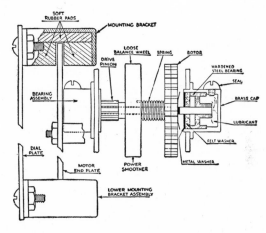

FIG. 6.131.   Cross-section of an electric clock mechanism.

A general indication that an electric clock motor is developing trouble will begin with noise during operation. This may be caused by tight bearings or loose gearing (Fig. 6.131).

Heating Appliances. A heating appliance, as the term is used here, means any electrical appliance which depends upon heat for its operation. In this group would be found such electrical appliances as the electric range, waffle iron, heating pad, and smoothing iron.

In operation all heating appliances employ the principle that an electric current passing through a resistance will produce heat. Alloyed iron wire is used to provide resistance in many heating appliances. The resistance, or heating element, as it is called, may be in wire or strip form, depending upon the appliance.

FIG. 6.132.   Single unit, three heat electric range.

In nearly every heating appliance the heating element is replaceable, and these elements may be purchased separately in any good electrical supply store. See Figs. 6.132–6.135.

Appliance Cords. Appliance cords may be divided into two general classifications: cords made especially for heating appliances, and cords for nonheating appliances. One reason for making this distinction is because heating appliances take relatively greater currents than nonheating appliances. All appliance cords should be flexible to permit easy bending without fracture. To ensure maximum flexibility appliance cords are made of stranded wires, that is, a number of small solid wires are twisted together to form a single conductor.

Fig. 6.133. Electric iron.

Heating Appliance Cords. If ordinary cotton and rubber insulation were used on the cord for supplying current to heating appliances, the insulation would overheat because of the relatively great current carried in the cord and there is the possibility of fire. Certainly a strong smell of smoldering rubber would appear.

To prevent such overheating, heater appliance cords with asbestos insulation are provided by the manufacturer. Cotton or silk may be used as an outer covering for the asbestos.

Heater cords are usually short cords not exceeding 6' in length. An easy way to recognize a heater cord, if the asbestos insulation is not visible, is by its bulkiness. It is somewhat larger than nonheater cords (Fig. 6.136).

Nonheater Appliance Cords. In the nonheater appliance cord category, there are a number of types of cords which may be used for a variety of purposes. A very handy cord is shown in Fig. 6.137.

It is known as "Rip-Cord" because one wire may be separated from the other by ripping. This avoids the removal of outer braid, such as would be

FIG. 6.134. Electric toaster.

FIG. 6.135. Electric percolator.

required with ordinary appliance cords.   Rip-Cord has another advantage. The overall insulation is very small in comparison with other types of appliance cords, and this makes it useful in lamp and small appliance wiring where

it is necessary to draw the appliance cord through small openings.

A durable cord for pendant or small appliance use is shown in Fig. 6.138. Notice that each copper wire (stranded) has a cotton wrap over which is placed rubber insulation.   Individual braids cover the rubber insulation and on top of that an overall braid keeps both wires in place.

A light duty, all-purpose nonheater appliance cord is shown in Fig. 6.139. It is used with a number of types of home appliances, such as vacuum cleaners, all kinds of mixers, and a garage portable extension lamp.   Each stranded base conductor is first cotton-wrapped, and then rubber-covered. A cotton filler is placed between each rubber-covered wire and a cotton braid which keeps both wires closely held together.   Over all is placed a rounded, smooth rubber covering.

FIG. 6.136.   Heater cord.
*Courtesy of Arrow Hart
Electric Co*

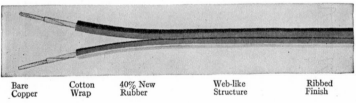

| Bare
Copper | Cotton
Wrap | 40% New
Rubber | Web-like
Structure | Ribbed
Finish |

FIG. 6.137.   Type PO-SJ Special "Rip-Cord."

Appliance Cord Attachments. Every appliance cord will require an attachment by means of which contact may be made with the existing house circuit, usually at a receptacle outlet.   Where no receptacle outlet is available, a connection may be made to a lamp socket by means of the fitting shown in Fig. 6.144. A pony female plug is shown in Fig. 6.143. This plug is used for light loads and is of light construction.   Its sturdier construction will permit usage with appliances which require a number of amperes for their operation, especially heater appliances.   In either case the lamp is removed from the light fixture, and the female attachment plug screwed in its place. A male plug on an appliance cord may then make contact with the house current by simply plugging it into the female plug. Be careful not to connect heavy-duty appliances to lamp sockets unless you are sure that the circuit can carry the current

Cord grip attachment plugs are very useful because an extra device is

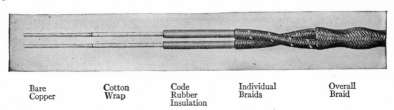

| Bare Copper | Cotton Wrap | Code Rubber Insulation | Individual Braids | Overall Braid |

FIG. 6.138.   Type PD cord.

provided which forms a sort of collar around the cord at the point where a cord enters the plug. Controlled by set screws, this collar device will prevent loosening and fraying of the outer cord covering.

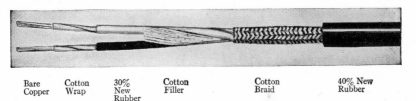

| Bare Copper | Cotton Wrap | 30% New Rubber | Cotton Filler | Cotton Braid | 40% New Rubber |

FIG. 6.139.   Type SV, vacuum cleaner cord.

Male plugs may be had with polarized prongs. These plugs are used for appliances which operate only when positive current flows through the

FIG. 6.140.   Rubber grip cap.   FIG. 6.141.   Grip cap.   FIG. 6.142.   Attachment cap.

appliance in one direction. It is impossible to force the plug into a receptacle any other way. Naturally, a polarized receptacle must be used with a polarized plug. See Figs. 6.140, 6.141, 6.142, and 6.145 for illustrations of cord caps.

Heater cords will require special plugs to make contact with the heater appliance.

A Bakelite heater plug is shown in Fig. 6.146. Its use gives the advantage of being able to disconnect the appliance from its cord when the appliance is not in use.

| FIG. 6.143. Pony female plug. | FIG. 6.144. Lamp socket fitting for appliance. | FIG. 6.145. Rubber cap (male plug) with cord grips. | FIG. 6.146.Bakelite heater plug. |

Many appliance cords and appliances do not have provision for turning the current on or off without releasing the male plug which is attached to the base receptacle. Several types of cord switches are available and are shown in Fig. 6.147. A cord switch may be inserted anywhere along the length of

FIG. 6.147. Cord switches. *Courtesy of Arrow Hart Electric Co.*

the attachment cord, preferably near the appliance, by breaking one wire through the cord switch.

Levolier Switches. Levolier switches are small, compact units built like watches and are attractively finished. A Levolier switch is easy to install and requires no extra wiring. They are made in three sizes from 3 to 10 ampere capacity and in the following types: single-pole, two circuit; series multiple; and three-way pull. See Figs. 6.148 and 6.149.

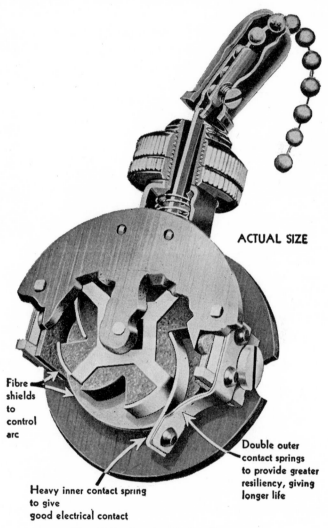

ACTUAL SIZE

Fibre shields to control arc

Heavy inner contact spring to give good electrical contact

Double outer contact springs to provide greater resiliency, giving longer life

FIG. 6.148. Interior of a Levolier switch.

Any light-duty electrical appliance that does not have a switch control as part of the appliance may be wired for switch control easily by using a Levo-

lier switch.   To install it, a hole is drilled in the appliance, at a point where
the Levolier switch is to be located, large enough to permit the threaded neck
of the switch to pass through from inside the fixture or appliance outward.
A locknut provided with the switch holds it firmly in place.   The switch is
then connected into the appliance circuit to obtain the desired control.

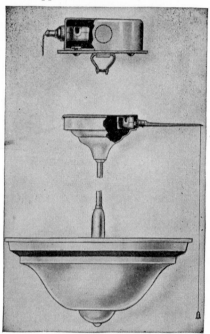

FIG. 6.149.   Levolier switch mounted in position.

FIXED ELECTRICAL EQUIPMENT

Motors . . . Drives . . . Generators . . . Storage   Batteries . . . Electric Lighting Plants . . . Sump Pumps . . . Water Pumps . . . Attic Ventilating Fans

This section will deal with certain major units of equipment, commonly found in the home and installed in relatively permanent positions. The equipment to be treated in this chapter includes refrigerators, small unit electric generating plants, and other fixed installations, as well as the electric motors, generators, storage batteries, and other units which are a part of these installations. They require relatively more current than other household equipment, and are sometimes called "power equipment" for that reason.

The details of design and the operating characteristics of this equipment vary widely, depending upon the specific service requirements and the objectives of the individual manufacturer. Moreover, a complete service job requires a knowledge of these details, as well as the use of specialized testing and repair apparatus. Therefore, this chapter will give general information about how this equipment operates and how it should be maintained, with as complete directions for trouble shooting as can be utilized profitably by the home owner.

Before proceeding to discuss the individual types of equipment, there are a number of general rules which apply in all cases. They are so important that the practical electrician must be conscious of them at all times. These rules are as follows:

1. All electrical devices must be supplied with the specific form of electrical energy of the proper kind of current (A.C. or D.C.) voltage and frequency. Some equipment may be designed to allow considerable variation in its supply and, in that case, it will be clearly designated.

2. All electrical devices must be well insulated.

3. All electrical devices must be given adequate electrical and mechanical protection by means of fuses, shearing pins, etc.

4. All electrical devices must be kept clean by a consistent program of

wiping, blowing with air, or exhausting by a vacuum cleaner.

5. All connections must be electrically and mechanically secure.

6. All moving parts must be unobstructed in their motion and properly lubricated.

Motors. In view of its wide use in electrical equipment, including oil burners, refrigerators, and many other devices, the electrical motor should be thoroughly understood, insofar as its proper maintenance is concerned. The general rules given above are especially pertinent in their application to electric motors. In particular, the importance of proper lubrication cannot be overemphasized. If the motor is of the self-oiling type, it must be kept sealed. If it has oil cups, they should be supplied with the proper oil. Motor bearings must be kept free of dust and dirt; they should be washed out with kerosene and then re-oiled. (*Note:* To avoid fire hazard from sparks all power must be turned off.) Motor collector rings and brush contact surfaces must be checked to make sure they are functioning properly, i.e., without excessive sparking.

When checking electric motors, attention should also be paid to motor accessory equipment, such as starting switches, relays, and other controls. Starting switches must be examined to make sure that they have no loose parts, and that they cut in and cut out properly. Contact surfaces in control equipment must be kept clean; they may be washed with carbon tetrachloride, and pits or burns in contacts may be removed with a fine point file and crocus cloth. Bearing points and movable parts should be oiled lightly with high grade oil. Controls should, of course, be kept free from dust and dirt, and their contact surfaces must "open and make" perfectly.

If, in spite of proper maintenance, there are evidences of motor trouble (the most common indication is overheating) the following common causes should be investigated:

1. The belt connected to the motor may be too tight.

2. The motor may be overloaded.

3. The motor may need oiling.

4. The motor may have shifted out of line.

5. The bearings may be dirty.

6. The oil rings may be jammed.

The following summary will be found useful in checking motor troubles:

1. If motor does not start and makes no sound, it usually indicates no electrical power. To test this, check for power at the switch, fuse boxes, control switch, control relays, or starting devices. If power is present check contact conditions and adjustments.

2. If motor does not start, but begins to smoke or smell, look for "frozen" bearings or a "stuck" part on the driven side. These parts must be freed by replacing bearings.

3. If motor does not start, but hums, this usually means one phase is open which may be caused by a broken wire, an open contact in the starting relay, or an open overload element or fuse.

4. If motor starts, but immediately stops, this usually indicates a power failure through an open circuit. The chief cause is an overload and may mean that the motor is too small. The open circuit may mean replacing a fuse, adjusting a relay contact, resetting the thermal overload, or repairing an open wire.

5. If the motor starts, but turns slowly, the cause is usually under voltage or overload. In the first case the wires feeding the machine must be checked for size and feed. In the second case, the load on the motor must be checked for its ease in turning. It may be necessary to free some part which is binding, reduce the load on the motor, or increase the size of the motor.

6. If the motor starts, but runs backward, it indicates that the machine was connected incorrectly, or that the supply to the machine has been reversed at some point. In the case of single phase machines starting connections may be reversed; in the case of multiphase motors, phases may be reversed and the wires will have to be transposed.

7. If the motor starts but becomes overheated, the condition may be attributed to several factors:

a. Dirt and poor ventilation. Obviously, correction of this condition will resolve itself into cleaning the motor and providing air circulation.

b. Overloading of motor. Trying to make it do more work than it was designed for. Reduce load or increase size of motor.

c. Internal friction. Parts rubbing due to worn shafts or bearing. This condition can be remedied by overhauling defective part.

d. In the case of the multiphase motors, lines may open and the motor tries to carry the load running on one phase. Checking of fuses, thermal and relay contacts will usually remedy this condition.

Drives. The electric motor may be connected directly to the equipment it operates, although belt drives are more commonly used. Units that are directly connected to the motor by a flexible coupling sometimes cause trouble when the load cushion (see Fig. 6.150) gives way. Replacement can easily be made by loosening the set screw, moving the part back on the shaft as in Fig. 6.150B, and inserting a new load cushion.

Belt drives commonly used in household equipment are the V-type and the flat-type. On V-belt drives, provision is usually made for tightening the belt by means of an adjustable base for the motor, which permits it to move. It is held in place by set screws, or by a spring under tension. Care should be exercised to see that the base moves freely, and that it is properly

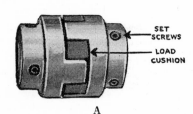

SET SCREWS

LOAD CUSHION

A   B

FIG. 6.150.   A. Flexible coupling for direct connection of electric motor.   B. Installation of a flexible coupling on shaft.

lubricated. On flat-belt drives, the shock is usually taken up by means of an idler pulley, which generally requires considerable attention. Tension is applied by weights or springs, which should have their adjustment checked frequently, to avoid their falling off or becoming so loose that they cause noise and vibration. The pulley must be lubricated, because if it runs dry it will wear.

Belt replacements should be of the same material, strength, ply, thickness, and width. The width of a belt should be $\frac{1}{2}''$ to $1''$ less than the face of the pulley on which it is mounted.

Generators. Electric generators are encountered by the home mechanic chiefly in automobiles and in home lighting units, although they are occasionally used for other purposes around the home. Their function is to convert mechanical energy, which is usually obtained from an internal combustion engine, into electrical energy for lighting or power. Thus, their function is the opposite of that of the electric motor, but their construction is similar, so that a generator may be considered as a motor operating in reverse and having the same requirements in the way of lubrication and other care. These requirements for generator care may be summarized briefly as follows:

1. Keep the generator properly oiled. Oil lightly and not too often. Do not apply too much oil.

2. Keep the generator clean.

3. Blow out the generator regularly.

4. Check brushes for wear and replace when necessary.

5. Keep contact surfaces clean.

6. Inspect all parts regularly to detect looseness before it has caused damage.

7. Inspect all connections regularly to make sure they are tight and properly insulated.

Generator troubles should be detected as soon as possible, because the proper functioning of other equipment depends on the generator. Storage batteries, in particular, may be severely damaged if they are overloaded through failure of the generator. The first step in testing the generator is to make sure that, when all lights and motors in the systems are shut off and all switches are open, no current flows in the circuit. This is conveniently done if an ammeter is installed in the circuit, by being sure that its reading is zero. Otherwise there is a short circuit somewhere in the system, which must be located and repaired. If no current flows when the equipment is disconnected, the causes of generator trouble must be sought elsewhere. The causes may be mechanical, such as worn bearings, dirty commutator, or worn brushes, or electrical, such as ineffective operation of the voltage regulator or generator cutout. Any of these troubles require the attention of a service man who has experience with the particular equipment, and tools and testing devices for working on it.

Storage Batteries. A storage battery produces electrical energy by a reversible chemical reaction. The type of battery in commonest use is the lead plate battery, which consists of a number of alternate positive or negative plates separated by sheets of wood or other insulating material. When the battery is charged, the positive plates are covered with lead peroxide and the negative plates with metallic lead. (For greater chemical reactivity, these materials are in a loose or spongy form.) Then, when the battery is filled with dilute sulphuric acid, and the plates are connected to an external circuit, the positive plates to one side of the circuit and the negative plates to the other, chemical reactions will take place in the battery, and they will cause a current to flow in the circuit. In these chemical reactions the lead on the negative plate combines with the sulphuric acid to form lead sulphate. Since sulphuric acid is much heavier than water, and since on discharge of the battery the acid combines with the material on the plates, leaving the water in the solution, it is easy to see that as the solution becomes lighter in weight (or lower in specific gravity) it indicates that the battery is discharging.

When the battery is charged, all the processes just described are reversed. The lead sulphate on the positive plates becomes lead peroxide again, the lead sulphate on the negative plates becomes metallic lead again, and both these reactions restore sulphuric acid to the solution, raising its specific gravity to the original value.

In a storage battery, the insulators between plates are called *separators*, and the solution of dilute sulphuric acid is called the *electrolyte*. The container that holds the electrolyte and supports the plates is called a *cell*. All the positive plates and all the negative plates in a cell are electrically connected in parallel and, therefore, the voltage of a cell is the same as that of a single pair of plates, which is about 2 volts. (See Chapter 1 for an explanation of parallel connection.) The number of plates in a cell is determined by the capacity that is desired of the battery, in amperes (momentary current) and ampere hours (current over a period of time). The number of cells assembled in a battery unit (in which the cells are connected in series) depends upon the voltage that is desired of the battery. Three cell units, yielding about 6 volts, are common and may, of course, be arranged in series with other units to give higher voltages.

General rules for the care and maintenance of storage batteries are as follows:

1. When servicing storage batteries, wear a rubber apron. The sulphuric acid electrolyte is destructive to clothing and, of course, to the skin.

2. Keep external parts of the battery clean. This includes terminals and cable connections. For cleaning, use a fairly stiff brush and a dilute solution in water and ammonia or bicarbonate of soda. When brushing, be careful to shield the eyes from spattering and, after cleaning is finished, be sure that all connections are tight.

3. Cover cable clamps, posts, connecting bars, and all other parts subject to corrosion with a mineral grease.

4. Make sure there are no leaks in the battery. Leaks are objectionable, even if they are in the sealing compound at the top, or at other points above the electrolyte level, because the acid may bubble out during charging.

5. Check the vent holes in the filler caps to make sure they are open. Never use a lighted match or other flame around storage batteries, because they produce hydrogen, an explosive gas.

6. Replace damaged or worn cables at once. They cause inefficient operation and may damage or ruin the battery and other equipment.

7. Check the level of electrolyte regularly, at least once a month. The liquid level should be at least $\frac{1}{4}''$ above the plates. Add distilled water to

bring the electrolyte up to this level. Never add any other liquid than distilled water. If you believe that acid should be added, because you know that some electrolyte has been lost, or for any other reason, turn this job over to a battery service man.

8. Check the specific gravity of the electrolyte at least once a month, but never within 6 hours after distilled water has been added. If the battery has a built-in float ball indicator, watch it according to the manufacturer's directions; if not, use a hydrometer to determine the specific gravity. The hydrometer reading should not be less than 1.250 at 70° F. If below this value, the battery should be charged. Do not charge too rapidly because this will cause overheating and gassing, and will knock the paste coating off the plates. Never allow batteries to remain discharged, because the lead sulphate on the plates becomes thick and adhesive, and the battery is impaired. Moreover, discharged batteries freeze more readily than charged ones. (Dilute sulphuric acid of 1.150 specific gravity freezes at 6° F.)

9. Be careful not to overcharge a battery, as this is equally or more injurious than a prolonged discharged condition. Excessive need for water indicates an overcharged condition, and the contact adjustment of the charging relay should be checked immediately.

Electric Lighting Plants. The essential elements of equipment in the average home or farm electric generating plant (Fig. 6.151) consist generally of a generator to produce the electrical energy, an engine to drive the generator, and storage batteries to store the electrical energy, to avoid the necessity for operating the engine and generator whenever electricity might be required. Generators and storage batteries have already been discussed in earlier sections of this chapter, so the present section will deal with the remaining machine used in small generating systems, the gasoline engine. While certain of the principles to be discussed, and practical suggestions to be made, apply to gasoline engines in general, this discussion will be directed particularly to the types used in home generating systems.

Most small, nonautomatic, or manually started generating units are driven by 2-cycle gasoline engines. These engines usually depend upon a magneto for the ignition current or spark. When the magneto is rotated, it generates a high tension current, which is transmitted by the wiring to the terminal of the spark plug. The plug carries the current through an insulator in its center to a spark gap at the other end in the cylinder and ignites the fuel mixture.

The 4-cycle engine is generally used with the self-starting and automatic units and differs from the 2-cycle engine in that it has an automatic starting mechanism, and that it usually has a crank case containing the lubricating medium, and a water system for cooling. Even though it does not require manual lubrication, except for certain points that may be specified by the manufacturers, it still requires attention to the oil system to see that it is changed periodically.

In addition to the engine itself, the coupling between the engine and the generator should be checked frequently. Moreover, many of these units have an external self-starter, for which service directions will also be given,

Fig. 6.151.   Home or farm electric generating plant.

even though some machines omit the self-starter, by carrying a set of low voltage starting windings in the field of the generator.

General maintenance directions quite properly begin with the statement that all electrical parts of the system be kept dry. Therefore, in humid weather, or under moist working conditions, the wires and porcelain of the spark plugs should frequently be wiped with a dry cloth. The magneto must be kept free of moisture and dirt, and its bearings must be lubricated regularly. The contact points on the magneto breaker should be checked regularly and cleaned with a fine point file. The 2-cycle engine depends for its lubrication upon oil that is introduced with the gasoline and it is most important the oil has the proper viscosity, and that it is mixed thoroughly with the gasoline. The carburetor strainer should be checked frequently to make sure it is clean. The idling screw on the carburetor should be checked for tightness and set for the most efficient idling speed. It is usually designed so that turning it toward the right will reduce the richness of the mixture and slow the engine, while turning it to the left will increase the richness of the mixture and speed up the engine. If the engine is equipped with an air cleaner on the carburetor inlet, it should occasionally be washed out with gasoline and re-oiled. In the 4-cycle engines in which there is a water cooling system, the water should be kept clean and, if it is to be operated at low temperatures, an antifreeze solution should be used.

In trouble shooting in engines, the first step is to make sure that fuel and air are supplied to the cylinders in proper proportions. If this is not the case, make sure that there is gasoline in the tank; then make sure that the fuel pump is operating properly; then check the fuel line, including the sediment bowl and the filter, to make sure there is no stoppage; then examine the fuel-tank cap, to make sure that the vent hole is clear; and finally, look for gas leaks or air leaks throughout the system.

If the trouble is not found in the fuel system, it may be in the ignition. First, make sure that the spark plugs are clean. If they "foul" constantly, the trouble may be due to the use of too rich a mixture, such as often results from overchoking on starting. Then make sure that the spark plugs are satisfactory.

Another common cause of ignition failure is loose connections in the ignition circuit which may cause spasmodic or intermittent operation. The next source of ignition trouble that should be checked is dirty or pitted distributor points, which should be replaced. Then check the ignition wiring to make sure there is not a worn, short-circuited, or broken lead. Then check the timing of the spark to make sure that it is not too far retarded.

Starting motors are used on some home lighting units, and should be checked if the engine fails to operate properly, and yet no trouble is found in the fuel or the ignition systems. If the starting motor does not spin, and the engine cannot be cranked, the starting gear is probably binding at the fly wheel. If the starting motor spins, there is probably mechanical trouble in some other part of the starter mechanism. Other obvious points to investigate for trouble in starting are the starter switch and the starter circuit. If the trouble still has not been found, the starting motor or its bearings may be damaged and probably require replacement.

Sump pumps (Fig. 6.152) are used to drain seepage from basements and underground floors and pits. They are generally installed in a pocket or sump located below the level of the surrounding floor for draining purposes. One type is operated by a float switch which turns the pump on whenever the water in the sump rises above a predetermined level. The other type does not have any moving control mechanism, but has a

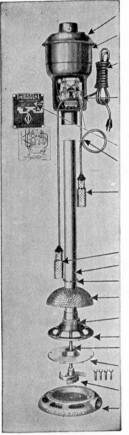

Automatic circuit breaker incorporated right in motor.

General Electric Motor with oil-sealed ball thrust bearing for vertical operation.

Cord with plug, for connecting to electrical supply line.

Relay box. Houses induction relay or "brain" of electrical control system. Relay switch starts and stops the motor, being operated by an infinitesimal induced electrical current. Diagram of control circuit is shown inside the cover of relay box. Plunger for manual starting. Motor will run as long as plunger is pushed up.

Clamp for adjusting height of upper electrode.

Electrodes are enclosed in an insulated metallic shield. Their function is to complete a circuit through the water carrying a tiny induced current of approximately 1–40 ampere to the induction relay controlling the motor.

The lower electrode.

Pump shaft housing of brass.

Snap ring holds strainer in position.

Extra large area brass strainer.

Special water-lubricated long-life bronze bearing.

Cast bronze pump casing.

Bronze, fully enclosed impeller shaft.

Brass plate forms suction side of pump.

Forged brass impeller, perfectly balanced.

Cast bronze pump base with discharge connection.

Fig. 6.152.   Sump pump.   View showing parts.   *Courtesy of General Electric Co.*

pair of immersion contacts through which a circuit starting the pump is completed when the water reaches the upper electrode.

General maintenance starts with keeping the drain inlet clear, because it often becomes clogged with dirt. The other parts should also be kept clean, the control contacts checked, and all parts properly lubricated. The general instructions for motor maintenance given earlier in this chapter apply to this motor also.

Water Pumps. Manually controlled and automatically controlled water pumps for domestic use usually consist of an electric motor driven pump which draws water from a well and raises it to a storage tank, which is frequently under pressure. In the automatic system, a pressure actuated electrical control starts the pump as soon as the pressure falls below a pre-set point.

The following rules govern the general maintenance of water pumps:

1. Make sure that intake strainers are clean.
2. Keep check valves tight.
3. Keep packing glands packed and tight.
4. Check piping for leaks.
5. Keep motor control clean and properly adjusted.
6. See that all moving parts are properly lubricated.
7. Check all contacts for proper operation.

FIG. 6.153. Close-up of attic ventilating fan installation.

Attic Ventilating Fans. Fans of the type illustrated in Figs. 6.153 and 6.154 are effective in hot weather for removing heated air from the home and replacing it with cooler outdoor air.   The time for operation is after the sun has set.   If the fan is employed for three or four hours in the evening,

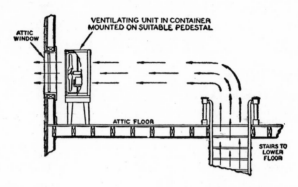

FIG. 6.154.   Schematic diagram of air circulation in house equipped with attic ventilating fan.

air temperatures inside the house may be reduced as much as 5° F. for the lower floors to 15 or 20° F. for the upper floors.

Attic ventilating fans usually require a $\frac{1}{4}$ or $\frac{1}{3}$ horsepower electric motor. Installation is simple, and the comfort that may be obtained is considerable. Maintenance consists only of oiling the fan shaft and motor bearings.

Chapter 8

OPEN WIRING ON INSULATORS—CONCEALED
KNOB AND TUBE WIRING—NON-METALLIC
SHEATHED CABLE WIRING

Armored cable and rigid conduit as wiring mediums provide metallic protection for the wiring, that is, wires are encased in flexible armor, in the method using armored cable, whereas wires are drawn through pipes, in the method using rigid conduit. A less expensive wiring method, particularly for insulated systems and surface wiring, is *Open Wiring on Insulators*.

OPEN WIRING ON INSULATORS

Open wiring on insulators differs from metallic-protected wiring methods in that the wiring for a little local circuit, a branch circuit, or a system is installed by means of individual wires, each supported and terminated according to the provisions of the National Electrical Code.

Open wiring on insulators, for the home mechanic, is an excellent medium by means of which he may practice and understand *circuiting*, that skill of the practical electrician which is the basis for properly connecting electrical fixtures, switches, receptacles and the like, according to the control desired.

Open wiring on insulators is used as a medium of instruction in many vocational schools, and the home mechanic may provide himself, if he so chooses, with a supply of cleats, knobs, tubes, woodscrews, switches, receptacles, and ⚡14 insulated lighting wire, and do each of the specimen jobs given in this section, upon a wooden backboard (temporary wiring board) of approximately kitchen table top size. As each job is completed and tested, it can be disassembled and the material used again.

Cleat Wiring. One method of open wiring on insulators is *cleat wiring*, which is used for exposed work, where wiring may be installed close to the surface being wired over, and where there is little likelihood of the wiring being disturbed.

Figure 6.155 shows a pair of porcelain, two-wire cleats. Note carefully that each cleat has a half groove near either end which is roughed, during manufacture, to grasp and hold securely an insulated wire when a pair of cleats are used in combination. Note also that holes are provided for screw

Fig. 6.155. Two-wire porcelain cleats. *Courtesy of Porcelain Products Inc.*

fastening. In installing open wiring on cleats, special care should be exercised to provide sufficient support for the wires so that they will not sag. More will be said about cleat supporting later.

Lamp Receptacle, with the Control at the Receptacle. Frequent use will be found for an additional lighting outlet, to be connected to an existing branch lighting circuit. Although the discussion which follows is confined to cleat wiring, the circuit wiring principle involved is the same for other methods of wiring, as, for example, armored cable, concealed knob and tube, Romex cable, and so on.

The simplest form of an electric circuit for a single lighting outlet is shown in Fig. 6.156. The illustration is called *a schematic diagram* and shows the outlet and conductor arrangement necessary for the little local circuit to be installed as a new lighting outlet.

Note the component parts of a simple lighting circuit, as shown in the schematic diagram. First, there must be a source of supply, normally 115 volts for lighting circuits. A source of supply may be obtained by connecting directly to a branch circuit cutout box (fuse box) or to any accessible point in a branch lighting circuit where it is possible to connect to a wire coming from the existing source of supply, and to the wire returning to the existing source of supply. Second, a means must be provided for lamp attachment to the circuit conductors. In Fig. 6.156, this means is indicated in symbol form as a lamp receptacle. Third, a wiring method must be employed which will safely conduct the electricity from the source of supply to the lamp receptacle and back again to the source of supply. In Fig. 6.156, the wiring method is shown as open wiring on cleats. In this simple project, the manner of controlling the flow of the electric current in the little lamp receptacle local circuit, that is, turning the lamp ON, or OFF, is provided for at the lamp receptacle, either by a key control, chain control, or some similar method.

In the foregoing discussion, mention was made of a wire coming from the source of supply to the lamp receptacle, and another wire returning from

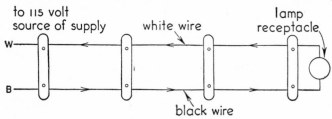

FIG. 6.156.   Lamp receptacle with the control at the fixture.

the lamp receptacle to the source of supply. For ease in circuit connecting, it is standard practice to use a *black* insulated wire, called the current-carrying wire, for the conductor coming from the source of supply, and a *white or gray* insulated conductor, called the return wire, for the wire returning the current from the lamp receptacle back to the source of supply.

In making connections for the little local circuit to the existing circuit, then, the black wire of the little local circuit would be connected to the black wire of the existing circuit, and the white wire of the little local circuit to the white wire of the existing circuit, or, to put it another way, color is connected to color, that is, black to black, and white to white.

The flow of current when the lamp control is in the ON position, as indicated by the arrowheads on the conductors shown in Fig. 6.156, will be from the source of supply by means of the current-carrying wire (black) to the lamp receptacle, through the lamp filament, and then back to the source of supply by means of the return (white) wire.

Lamp Receptacle Controlled by a Single-pole Switch. Very often it will be found undesirable to limit the means of control to a lamp receptacle, especially when the lighting outlet is located beyond normal reach. It may be more convenient, and certainly more practical, to provide a switch control, separate and away from the lamp receptacle.

A schematic diagram illustrating the wiring, devices, and the manner of cleat supporting for a lamp receptacle controlled by a single-pole switch, which is located some distance from the lamp receptacle, is shown in Fig. 6.157. Note first that the single-pole switch breaks the current-carrying, or black, wire. With this single exception, the little local circuit shown in Fig. 6.157 is similar to the little local circuit shown in Fig. 6.156. When the single-pole switch is in the ON position, current will flow from the source of supply by means of the black wire, through the blade contact of the

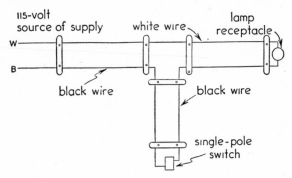

Fig. 6.157. Lamp receptacle controlled by a single-pole switch.

switch, again by means of a black wire to the lamp receptacle, then through the lamp filament, and thence back again to the source of supply by means of the white, or return, wire, thus completing the circuit. When the switch is in the OFF position, the little local circuit, of course, is open, or inoperative, and no current will flow.

Standard Practices in Cleat Wiring. Cleat wiring, like any other wiring method, should be installed according to standard practices, normally directed by the National Electrical Code. Since it is not possible to discuss every requirement in cleat wiring here, we will touch briefly on those which apply to little local installations.

Cleats should be spaced no farther than 4′, 6″ apart, and closer than that where necessary. A necessary point for closer cleat support is shown in Fig. 6.157, where the black wire, running as a pair with the white wire from the source of supply, changes direction in going to and from the switch cation. Note carefully how three pairs of cleats are employed, in close oximity and at right-angles to each other, where a wire changes direction. Conductors should be spaced a minimum of 2½" apart in all exposed, en wiring installations, and should be at least ½" from the surface wired er. Cleats should be placed to support each conductor within 6" of a lice and, where possible, within 6" of every terminating point, such as a mp receptacle, switch, or convenience receptacle. The best policy to be uided by in supporting open wiring, when in doubt whether or not to put an additional support, is to put one in and be on the safe side. Note the pporting cleats near the switch and the lamp receptacle in Fig. 6.157.

Lamp Receptacle. A lamp receptacle is used to provide an easy means hereby a common lamp, or bulb, of the screw-shell type, can be connected

Fig. 6.158A. Surfolet lamp receptacle.   Fig. 6.158B. Surfolet tumbler switch.

o circuit conductors. A surface type lamp receptacle is illustrated in Fig. .158A. Lamp receptacles for exposed wiring on insulators may be had ith key-control, pull-chain control, or, for use with local switches, no current control at the lamp receptacle whatsoever.

Points to remember when installing a surface type lamp receptacle are: 1) The lamp receptacle should be firmly and securely mounted; (2) the hell of the lamp receptacle should be connected to the return (white) wire f the circuit. The manufacturer identifies the connecting terminals of amp receptacles, as well as other fixtures, by providing a nickel-plated erminal screw for the shell connection, and a brass screw for the lip, or enter-point, connection (black wire). We should also remember that ires are terminated around terminal screws in the same direction that the crew turns to tighten, and that no excess bare copper wire should extend eyond the head surface of the terminal screw.

Switch. A switch suitable for open wiring on insulators, exposed installations, is shown in Fig. 6.158B. The same installation precautions discussed

for a lamp receptacle apply to the installation of a surface switch. Switches
are usually mounted 4′ to center from the floor.

**Three Lamp Receptacles Connected in Parallel, with the Control at
Individual Receptacles.** More often than not, the need will arise for two

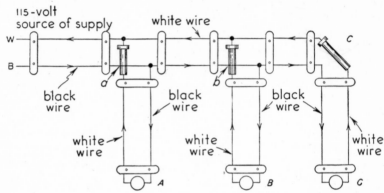

FIG. 6.159. Three lamp receptacles connected in parallel, with the control at each
receptacle.

three, or more outlets to be used for lighting purposes, all to be connected
to the same little local circuit. The schematic diagram shown in Fig. 6.159
illustrates how the conductors are arranged, supported, and the lamp receptacles connected so as to ensure full voltage (115 volts) being supplied to
each of the three lamp receptacles.

Splices (represented by heavy dots in the illustration) are necessary to
provide individual circuits for lamp receptacles A and B, where they attach
to the main circuit wires. The method used to make single-branch, or tap,
splices, such as are used here, is discussed in detail in the chapter entitled
"General Operations in Electrical Work."

An important point to note in the diagram shown in Fig. 6.159 is the
means provided to protect the lower conductor where one wire crosses

FIG. 6.160. Porcelain tube.
Courtesy of Porcelain Products Inc.

another, as at *a*, and again at *b*. Porcelain
tubes are used for this purpose (see Fig.
6.160). Protective tubes may be had in 3″,
4″, and 6″ lengths, according to the install-
ment need. Another point requiring attention in the same diagram (Fig. 6.159) is the

use of a porcelain tube on the longest span of wire where a 90-degree, or
right-angle, turn is made in the direction of the wiring, thus ensuring proper

protection since the wires will be closer together at the turning point than the 2½″ separation required by standard practice.

One more example of cleat wiring should suffice before we consider Knob Wiring, which is another method of open wiring on insulators. Figure 6.156 illustrated a wiring diagram for a lamp receptacle controlled at the receptacle; Fig. 6.157, a lamp receptacle controlled by a single-pole switch; and now, in Fig. 6.161, a single-pole switch controlling a lamp receptacle, with a convenience receptacle (live outlet) in the same circuit.

According to requirements, the switch should control the lamp receptacle but not the convenience receptacle. The convenience receptacle, then, is

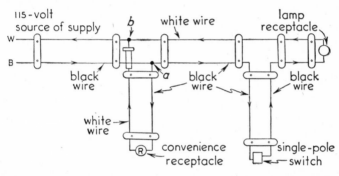

Fig. 6.161. Single-pole switch controlling a lamp receptacle, with a utility receptacle in the same circuit.

to be "alive" at all times, whereas the lamp receptacle is to be controlled by the operation of the single-pole switch. If we examine the schematic diagram shown in Fig. 6.161, it will be noted that current will flow from the source of supply by means of the black, current-carrying wire to the splice at *a*, where it continues via black wire to the convenience receptacle, through the portable electrical appliance which attaches to the convenience receptacle, then to splice *b*, by means of a white wire, and from this point back to the source of supply via the return (white) wire. No switch or other device, aside from the convenience receptacle itself, interrupts the flow of current in this little local circuit, which is "alive" at all times.

The rest of the circuit shown in Fig. 6.161, that is, the lamp receptacle controlled by a single-pole switch, is a repetition of the diagram discussed in Fig. 6.157, and is circuited in the same manner.

Knob Wiring. Knob wiring may be used for both exposed and concealed installations because knobs support a conductor a greater distance away from the surface being wired over than do cleats. Fig. 6.162 shows two types of split knobs; Fig. 6.162*A* illustrates a nail split knob, and Fig. 6.162*B*, a screw split knob. When nails are used to mount knobs, the nails should not be smaller than 10 penny. Cushion washers should be

A   *B*

FIG. 6.162.   Split knobs.   *Courtesy of Porcelain Products Inc.*

used with nail knobs. When screws are used to mount knobs, the screws should be of a length sufficient to penetrate the wood to a depth equal to at least one-half the full height of the knob.

Simple Lamp Receptacle Circuit. Electrically, the simple lamp receptacle circuit shown in Fig. 6.163 and that shown in Fig. 6.156 are the same. Each depends upon a current-carrying (black) wire and a return (white) wire from-and-to a 115-volt source of supply for operation. The difference

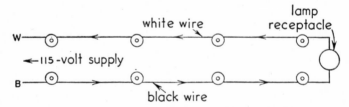

FIG. 6.163.   Simple lamp receptacle circuit—knob wiring.

between the two is in the method of wiring employed. Figure 6.156 illustrated cleat wiring, whereas Fig. 6.163 illustrates knob wiring.

Knob Supporting. Knobs, like cleats, should be spaced no farther apart than 4′ 6″, and closer together when necessary. Cleats supported wires in pairs; knobs, it will be noticed by referring to Fig. 6.163, support wires individually.

Wiring is not usually run in one direction. It will be necessary, frequently, to make a 90-degree, or right-angle, turn to change the direction of a run.

The manner in which a 90-degree turn is made with knob supports is shown in Fig. 6.164.

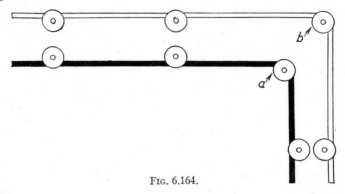

FIG. 6.164.

The minimum spacing, 2½″ apart for conductors in exposed open wiring, must be maintained when turns in the wiring are made, as well as in straight runs. Note the knobs at *a*, and *b*, in Fig. 6.164, which are so placed as to

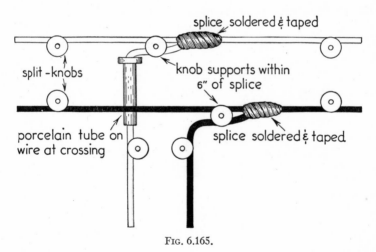

FIG. 6.165.

ensure the required 2½″ conductor spacing in making the turns for each wire.

A branch splice is necessary where one wire is to tap on to another wire anywhere along its length. Figure 6.165 illustrates the manner in which knobs are employed to support branch splices. Note the use of both grooves in one knob; one groove supports the main wire, and the remaining groove of the same knob supports the tapping wire.   Note also that this double-supporting knob is located within 6″ of the splice, to conform to standard

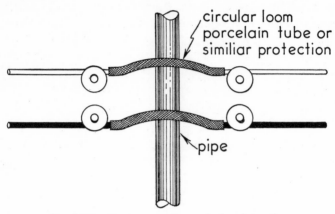

circular loom
porcelain tube or
similiar protection

pipe

FIG. 6.166.   Passing over pipe or similar obstruction.

practice.   Another point to be noted is that where one wire crosses another, as the white wire crosses the black wire in Fig. 6.165, a porcelain tube is used to protect the wire nearest to the surface being wired over from possible injury, at the crossing point.   To keep this tube in place, a knob is installed close to where the wire leaves the tube.

In installing open wiring, whether while using cleats or knobs, there is

FIG. 6.167.   Circular loom.

likely to be encountered a metallic obstruction, such as a water pipe, iron supporting beam, or the like.   An example of such a situation is shown in Fig. 6.166, where a water pipe has been encountered in making a run. Wires passing over or under metallic objects should have additional protection to the insulation on the wires themselves.   Porcelain tubes of sufficient length to clear the object on both sides may be used, or a sleeve such as a circular loom (see Fig. 6.167) may be employed to give each wire the extra protection required. Particular attention should be given to ensure that knobs are placed on both sides of the obstruction, so as to slightly belly-up, or down, the protected wiring.

Three Lamp Receptacles, Each Controlled by a Single-pole Switch. Independent control of lighting outlets, either at the fixture itself or by switch control located in the same room or space with the outlet, is characteristic of residential and small-house wiring. Figure 6.168 illustrates a schematic diagram showing how three lamp receptacles, each controlled

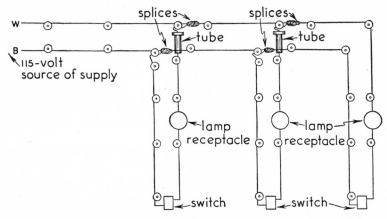

FIG. 6.168.   Three-lamp receptacles, each controlled by a single-pole switch.

independently by a local switch, would be installed in exposed knob wiring. The most important thing to remember in any exposed, open wiring installation is to *space and support the wiring adequately.*

Feeding a Little Local Circuit Through the Switch Location. In all the specimen schematic diagrams presented thus far for cleat and knob wiring, involving independent control by a single-pole switch, an assumption was made that the manner of wiring was from the source of supply through the lamp outlet, and then to the switch location.

A situation may be encountered where a part of the new installation, consisting of a lamp receptacle, a single-pole switch to control the lamp receptacle, and a convenience receptacle, is to form a little local circuit of its own, with the source of supply entering the little local circuit through the switch location, as compared to entry through the lamp receptacle location, as heretofore.

Figure 6.169 shows how a little local circuit, such as was described in the previous paragraph, would be connected and installed to an existing branch circuit. Note that a current-carrying wire (black) is spliced to the current-

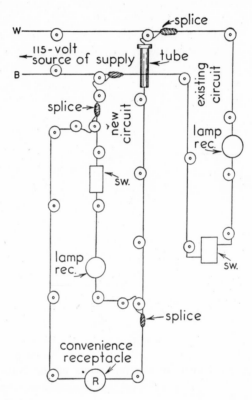

Fig. 6.169.   Feeding a little local circuit through the switch location.

carrying wire of the existing branch circuit, which is then carried to the switch, and also, by splicing again before the switch, to the convenience receptacle. Another black wire is run from this same switch to the lamp receptacle which it controls, and then a return wire (white) is run from the convenience receptacle, and the lamp receptacle, to the return wire of the existing branch circuit, where it is spliced to provide a return to the source of supply.

CONCEALED KNOB AND TUBE WIRING

Concealed knob and tube wiring is a method of wiring suitable for small-house installations, where a completely insulated interior wiring system is desirable. Few tools are required to perform installation practices using this wiring method.

The wiring method consists of individual conductors mounted on split knobs fastened to the sides and tops of wooden beams, joists, studs, and the like, and tube protection where these same conductors pass through the construction, so that the entire installation, with the exception of fixture outlets, switches, etc., is out of view when the structure is completed.

Courtesy of Porcelain Products Inc.

A	B	C
Deep outlet box.	Plaster ring for outlet box.	Shallow ceiling box.

FIG. 6.170.

In the discussion of open wiring on insulators, cleat and knob wiring, minimum spacing distance between conductors for exposed installations was given as $2\frac{1}{2}''$. For concealed knob and tube installations standard practice, as recommended by the provisions of the National Electrical Code, requires a minimum of $3''$ between conductors. Knobs and tubes are used for all concealed supporting to obtain this required minimum conductor spacing.

Insulated boxes (non-metallic) are used with insulated systems. Figure 6.170A shows a type of deep outlet box which provides individual entrance for conductors. Figure 6.170B shows a collar attachment for the outlet box in Fig. 6.170A, which can be used to advantage where ceilings are to be plastered. Figure 6.170C shows a shallow ceiling outlet box, which can be used in places where the construction will not permit the use of a deep outlet box.

Switch and convenience receptacle boxes for concealed installations are similar in appearance (see Fig. 6.171). Switches are usually mounted 4′ to center from the finished floor, and convenience receptacles (except in kitchen and dinette spaces), are mounted to clear the baseboard.

Standard Installation Practices.   Mounting Outlet Boxes.   Ceiling outlet box locations are found by establishing a center point between the space length and the space width.   This center point may occur on the under, or room, side of an overhead beam, or, as frequently happens, will come between two beams in the space known as a bay.   If the room center is established under a beam face, ceiling outlet box mounting is no problem at all—

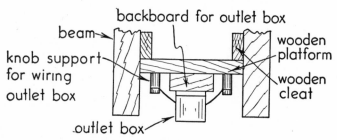

Fig. 6.172.   Ceiling box mounting and knob supports for wires.

a shallow box is fastened directly to the beam face with woodscrews.   When the room center falls in a bay between two beams, some preparation is necessary to provide a suitable mounting for the box.

Figure 6.172 shows a mounting for a ceiling outlet box, where the room center falls between two beams.   Wooden cleats, at least 1″ in thickness, are nailed against each beam-side in the bay.   A wooden platform, again, at least 1″ in thickness, is nailed to the wooden cleats.   A wooden backboard, slightly larger than the circumference of the outlet box, is then nailed to the platform, at the room center point, and the outlet box fastened to this platform by means of woodscrews.   The entire mounting should be arranged so that the room face of the outlet box will project about ½″ below the room side of the beam face, which will bring the outlet box near to the finished ceiling line.

Note in Fig. 6.172 how the use of a platform and a backboard provides a well against which conductors can be knob-supported, in accordance with

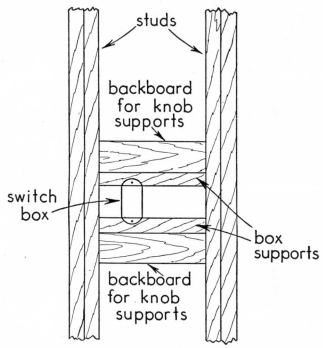

studs

backboard for knob supports

switch box

box supports

backboard for knob supports

Fig. 6.173.   Switch box mounting.

standard practice of individual conductor supports within 6″ of every box. Where it is not possible to support conductors within 6″ of an outlet box, circular loom or similar protection should be used on each conductor from the final knob support to the box entrance.

Switch Box Mounting. We said previously that switch boxes are placed 4′ from the finished floor to center and are usually located near, or adjacent to, door openings on the handle side of the door swing. Switch boxes may be secured in place by means of Kruse Strips between studs, or, as shown in Fig. 6.173, mounted on wooden strips, at least 1″ in thickness, running between the studs above and below the switch box. Backboards are placed above and below these box mounting strips (where more than two conductors enter a box) to provide a means of knob support for conductors within 6″ of the switch box.

Convenience Receptacle Boxes.   Convenience receptacle boxes are mounted much in the same manner as discussed in the foregoing paragraph for switch boxes. They may be installed so that the length rests horizontally, or vertically, as desired; however, the horizontal installation is most common and especially desirable where finished room walls are to be paneled and styled.

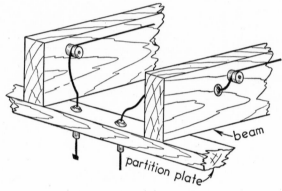

FIG. 6.174.   Conductor supports and protection.

Conductor Supporting and Protection.   In concealed knob and tube wiring individual conductors are run along the sides of beams, joists, studs and the like, and through these members where the wiring goes contrary to the construction. Separating, supporting, and protecting are cardinal points of importance in this kind of an installation.

Several important wiring points may be learned by studying Fig. 6.174. First, standard practice dictates the limitation of one conductor supported against a beam-side. Conductors should be run along the middle part of the beam-side, rather than favoring either top or bottom faces, to keep the wiring away from possible damage. Second, where a conductor passes through a beam, a porcelain tube is inserted in the bored hole (which is bored at a slight downward angle to prevent the tube from slipping out) and, where the conductor changes direction upon emerging from the tube, a knob support is placed close to the tube. Third, it will be noted in Fig. 6.174 that a tube is employed to protect a conductor which passes from a beam-side into a partition, through the overhead partition plate.

Figure 6.175 illustrates the manner in which conductors should be protected when they pass through the construction, from one floor to another floor. Note the use of double tubes, on each conductor, one tube being

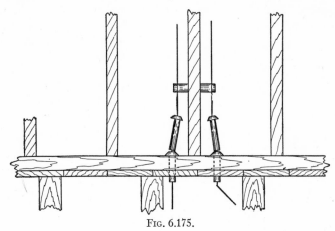

FIG. 6.175.

inserted in the bored hole of the lower partition plate, and a second tube on top of this first one to afford the conductor maximum protection against dust accumulation.

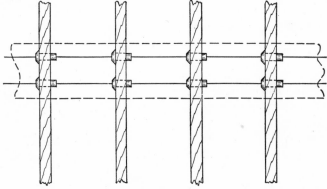

FIG. 6.176A.

Conductors passing metal, such as pipes, iron beams, brackets and so on, should be protected by circular loom, or the equivalent, where conductors pass over or under, and knob supports should be installed at both ends of the loom to keep it in place.

Running board protection is required in an unfinished attic, where conductor runs are made within 7' of the floor. Figure 6.176*A* shows a run of conductors passing through a series of rafters, such as would be encountered

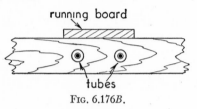

running board

tubes

FIG. 6.176*B*.

in the unfinished floor of an attic. The same illustration could represent roof supports for a peaked-roof. In either event, a board of greater width than the span of the conductors should be fastened over the run from end to end. In Fig. 6.176*A*, the running board is shown by means of broken

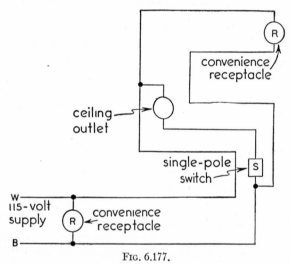

R

convenience receptacle

ceiling outlet

single-pole switch

S

W
115-volt supply

R convenience receptacle

B

FIG. 6.177.

lines. Figure 6.176*B* shows a cross-sectional view of the running board and its relation to the wiring being protected.

Typical Knob and Tube Concealed Installation. Figure 6.177 shows a schematic diagram of a little local circuit which is to be installed for a new one-room extension being made to a finished house.

The installation, using concealed knob and tube wiring as the wiring method, consists of two convenience receptacles, a ceiling outlet, and a

ingle-pole switch to control the ceiling outlet. The source of supply for
he new circuit is to be taken from an accessible outlet in the existing sys-
em, and it will enter the new circuit through a convenience receptacle
outlet.

An examination of the schematic diagram will indicate that two conductors are required from the existing source of supply to the first con-

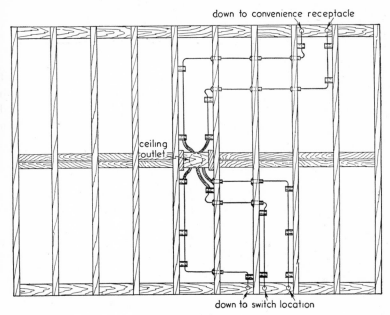

down to convenience receptacle

ceiling outlet

down to switch location

Fig. 6.178.

venience receptacle; two conductors from this convenience receptacle to
the new switch; three conductors from the switch to the new ceiling outlet;
and two conductors from the ceiling outlet to the second convenience
receptacle.

Figure 6.178 shows a view of how the overhead portion of the installation
drawn schematically in Fig. 6.177 would appear if we were to look down
upon it after completion of the wiring. Note the separation of conductors
(only one conductor is fastened to the side of each beam) as shown in the
illustration. Where a conductor passes through a beam or plate, a porcelain
tube is inserted in the bored hole and then the conductor is passed through
the tube. At points where conductors emerge from tubes and then make a

90-degree turn, it will be noted that a knob support is placed close to where each conductor leaves its tube. Sufficient knob supports are placed along straight runs to comply with the 4½′ regulation, made on the beam-sides, to ensure rigid conductor supporting.

NON-METALLIC SHEATHED CABLE WIRING

Thus far in this chapter we have discussed Open Wiring on Insulators for exposed work, both cleat and knob wiring, and Concealed Knob and Tube Wiring. Non-metallic sheathed cable wiring is another low-cost wiring method suitable for residences and small buildings and is particularly appropriate for use on insulated systems.

Since non-metallic sheathed cable contains wires in pairs, it is usable in both old- and new-house wiring. In new-house wiring such cables should be supported by approved staples, straps or similar fittings, without damage to the cables. Cables should be fastened in place at least every 4½′, and within 12″ of all outlet, switch, and receptacle boxes. In concealed, fin-

Fig. 6.179.   Non-metallic sheathed cable.

ished-house work, cables may be "fished" from outlet to outlet in the concealed spaces of the building without such supporting.

Non-metallic sheathed cables in exposed work should closely follow the building surface or running boards. Non-metallic sheathed cables should be protected from mechanical injury by conduit, pipe, or guard strips. When non-metallic sheathed cable passes through from one floor to another floor, it should be protected by rigid conduit or pipe extending at least 6″ above the floor. Here, then, is a wiring method which could be used for surface extensions where insulated systems are employed.

Bends in non-metallic sheathed cable wiring should be so made that the protective covering of the cable will not be injured, fractured, or otherwise damaged during installation. No cable bend shall have a radius less than 5 times the diameter of the cable. This is an important point to consider, as wiring troubles develop from closely made bends, such as wire fracture, broken outer insulation, and the like.